Animals Grow

Teacher's Guide

D1557737

Pan-Canadian Science Place Team

Gary Cross   Denise MacDonald   Wayne Stewart

Xavier Fazio   Susan Martin   Brian Veitch

Don Kelly   Kathleen Rosborough   Barbara Wall

Jo-Anne Lake   Judy Willson

British Columbia Advisors

Sandra Ball

Marjean Brown

David Hockley

Gowa Kong

Bev Parslow

Scientific Accuracy

Cendrine Huemer

Canadian Nature Federation

Scholastic Canada Ltd.

Published by
Scholastic Canada Ltd. 175 Hillmount Road, Markham, Ontario, L6C 1Z7

Cover photo: George K. Peck/Ivy Images

Animals Grow Teacher's Guide
ISBN 0-7791-3495-8

Printed and bound in Canada.

10 9 8 7 6 5 4 3 2   04 05 06 07 08

Contents

This icon indicates content related to Aboriginal peoples.

Welcome to Pan-Canadian Science Place

Pan-Canadian Science Place is the science program that gives you everything you need to turn your classroom into a science place.

Children are naturally curious about the world around them, and Pan-Canadian Science Place takes advantage of their eagerness to ask questions. In fact, as you will notice in the table of contents, we ask a lot of questions too. We want to give children as many hands-on science experiences and opportunities to investigate as possible.

All the components of the Pan-Canadian Science Place work together to support you and your children in your explorations of the world around you. You don't need to worry about not knowing the answers to all their questions. Together, you and your children will discover the answers—and probably come up with even more questions!

Pan-Canadian Science Place encourages children to construct meaning out of their own experience—it does not hand them the answers. We believe that interpreting and communicating their learning is as important to children's understanding as the explorations themselves.

While engaging children, the lessons build on prior knowledge and lead from one lesson to another. Each lesson is built on the same foundations: activating prior knowledge and engaging children's interest; exploring a concept with open-ended or directed explorations and information; and applying what children have learned to their world.

The Pan-Canadian Science Place Student Books, Teacher's Guides, science equipment packs, and library collection all work together to make science learning a fun and successful experience.

Kindergarten	My World (Three units together in a Lapbook)		
	Characteristics of Living Things	Properties of Objects and Materials	Surroundings
Grade 1	**It's Alive** Needs of Living Things	**Let's Move** Forces and Motion	**Earth Watch** Daily and Seasonal Changes
Grade 2	**Animals Grow** Animal Growth and Changes	**Matter, Matter Everywhere** Properties of Matter	**Air and Water** Air, Water, and Soil
Grade 3	**Watch It Grow!** Plant Growth and Changes	**Build It Up** Materials and Structures	**Stars and Planets** Stars and Planets
Grade 4	**Healthy Habitats** Habitats and Communities	**Light and Sound** Light and Sound	**Weatherwise** Weather
Grade 5	**Body Works** Human Body	**Putting It in Motion** Forces and Simple Machines	**Rockhound** Renewable and Non-Renewable Resources
Grade 6	**Variety of Life** Diversity of Life	**Turn It On** Electricity	**Extreme Environments** Extreme Environments

Components of Pan-Canadian Science Place

Student Books

Pan-Canadian Science Place Student Books are designed with children in mind. The books help children understand how the science they are learning applies to their lives. The type is large, and the instructions are numbered, clear, and easy-to follow. The photographs and illustrations are bright and colourful, and support children as they work through the explorations. Each book also has a glossary of terms for the unit.

Teacher's Guides

Pan-Canadian Science Place Teacher's Guides provide teachers with everything they need to manage their science program easily and enjoyably. The consistent three-step lesson plans—**Activate, Explore,** and **Apply**—make the lessons easy to use at a glance. Each lesson includes expectations, assessment options linked to expectations, background information, ideas to activate prior knowledge and introduce concepts, sample answers to questions, step-by-step support for explorations, expected exploration results, activities to apply the learning to situations outside the classroom, reproducible pages, support for struggling or ESL learners, and ideas to extend the learning and to integrate science into other areas of the curriculum.

Equipment Pack

For every unit of Pan-Canadian Science Place, an equipment pack is available. Except for a few easily gathered materials (newspaper, cardboard, dish soap), everything you need for explorations in the unit is provided. No more scrounging around from other teachers. All the equipment you need is in one place: wire, soil, rocks, magnifiers, sand, butterfly larva and food, and much more.

Science Library Collection

A collection of books, organized by strand, is a source of reference and additional activities for the science concepts for each grade. The colourful and engaging books are at a variety of reading levels to support all the children in the classroom. General suggestions for using the collection are included in the Program and Assessment Guide.

Program and Assessment Guide Grades 1–3

The educators who bring you Science Place wanted to provide teachers with all the support they need to run a successful science program in their class. The Program and Assessment Guide sets out their beliefs in science learning so you will understand the flow and focus of the program. It supports you as you implement the scientific inquiry and design process as the model for science discovery in your class. Also, background on Assessment and Evaluation of science learning is provided, as well as the strategies and tools you will need to assess your children's learning such as rubrics and checklists. Classroom management suggestions and strategies for using the books from the library collection are also included.

Features of the Teacher's Guide

T he Pan-Canadian Science Place Teacher's Guide has many features that help you plan and carry out a successful lesson.

In this Lesson
• a preview of the lesson

Outcomes
• specific outcomes from the B.C. Science Curriculum
• outcomes that are not the focus are listed by code

Getting Organized
• classroom management for the lesson:
- time—the time necessary for each step of the lesson
- advance preparation—notice if you need to prepare or send away for material later in the unit
- safety—possible areas of concern and how to avoid or deal with them

Content Background
• science information about the concept to support teachers

Activate
• discussion, demonstration, or activity to introduce and engage students in the lesson

---

Lesson 13

What Happens to Water After You Use It?

Student Book pages 28–29

In this lesson: Children identify substances that pollute water and discuss how the disposal of waste water can affect living things.

Specific Outcomes

Children will have opportunities to:
• distinguish ways in which air, water, and soil are used by living things (T2)
• identify the importance of clean water for living things and suggest ways to conserve water (T3)
• make observations and measurements using the senses and appropriate tools (P1)
• classify objects, events, and organisms (P2)
• collaborate with others in scientific investigations (P3)
• predict possible outcomes given a set of conditions and events (P5)
• ask questions and develop plans to investigate those questions (P6)
• make inferences about events or circumstances directly observed (P7)

Assessment

• Listen to children's responses as they discuss the questions posed in the Explore section about the photographs on Student Book page 29. Do children's responses indicate an awareness of the effects of polluted or untreated water to the health of people, other animals, and plants? (T2, T3, P1, P2)
• Review children's completed research. How well are children able to communicate their findings through words or pictures? How well were children able to stay on topic? (T2, T3, P1, P2, P3, P5, P7)

• Listen to children's responses as they discuss and report on the challenge outlined in the Think! section. Are children able to identify ways in which people pollute water in their homes? Are children able to devise a plan for reducing water pollution in their homes? Are children able to describe the steps involved? How successful were children in helping family members recognize that water is a scarce resource to be used wisely? (T2, T3, P1, P2, P3, P5, P6, P7)

Getting Organized

Advance Arrange for someone from your local water works department to speak to the class about how waste water is treated.

Materials: paper; pencils

Suggested Grouping: class/groups

Suggested Time: Activate 10–15 min; Explore 20–30 min; Apply 40–60 min

Lesson Vocabulary

chlorine: a chemical that is used to destroy germs in water

sewage: waste matter

CURIOSITY PLACE

The first water pipes in North America were made of hollowed-out logs. Today water pipes are made of concrete, metal, and plastic.

86 | Lesson 13: What Happens to Water After You Use It?

Content Background

W hen people use water, they sometimes leave impurities in it, making the water unfit for other uses. This waste water, which includes particles of human waste, garbage, and other contaminants, is known as sewage. When it's not disposed of properly, it causes damage to the environment.

Sewage goes through several different stages of processing at treatment plants. First the water is passed through a screen, leaving larger particles of matter behind. The liquid is allowed to settle in a sedimentation tank, so that more of the solid matter sinks to the bottom as sludge. The effluent portion is returned to the waterways or put through further treatment. Such further processing includes adding chemical disinfectants such as chlorine to the water, or running it through microscopic filters.

Some houses, particularly in rural areas, contain their own waste treatment facilities in the form of septic tanks. These tanks are concrete or steel containers which are buried under the ground. Sewage is carried along pipes from the house to the septic tank. Solid matter sinks to the bottom of the tank, becoming sludge. Bacteria in the sewage breaks down the sludge, converting it into gas and humus. The liquid portion, known as effluent, passes through a leaching field where more impurities are removed and gradually absorbed into the surrounding soil.

Troubleshooting

You might want to draw a simple flow chart on the board to show how water moves in and out of our homes.

Activate

What do we know? What do we want to know?

Describing Water

Have children recall the ways they use water. Ask them:

How does water look before you use it? (Answers will vary. Possibilities include "clear" "silvery".)

How does water look after you wash your hands and face? (Answers will vary. Possibilities include "soapy," "dirty".)

How does water look after you brush your teeth? (The water looks white.)

How does water look after you wash the dishes? (Answers will vary. Possibilities include "soapy," "orange," "grey".)

Would you want to use this water again? Why? (Accept all reasonable explanations.)

Preconceptions

Children may not realize that they pollute water every time they use it to brush their teeth, shampoo their hair, and so on. Use the following demonstration to help children understand that water is spoiled whenever anything is added to it. Fill a bowl with water and show it to the children. Explain to children that the water is clean. Then using liquid soap, wash your hands in it. Show the bowl to the children. Explain to children that the water is no longer clean because the soap and dirt from your hands have been added to it.

Lesson 13: What Happens to Water After You Use It? | 87

Assessment
• a variety of assessment options (observation, assessment tasks, tests, reviewing written work, interviews) and tools (rubrics and checklists) are provided to help you gather and evaluate information about your students' learning
• linked directly to outcomes

Curiosity Place
• interesting science facts that teachers may want to share with students

Lesson Vocabulary
• words in the lesson that may be new to students are defined in language that can be shared with students and augment the vocabulary provided in the student text Glossary

Preconceptions
• possible areas of confusion or where some students may have inaccurate understanding

Troubleshooting
• tips to help the activity run smoothly or notice of what may go wrong in an exploration and why

Explore
- ideas to introduce the Exploration to students
- step-by-step support for the Exploration and what to expect at each step

Apply
- examples and activities to apply the learning to real-life situations

Integrating Science
- suggestions for connecting science with other areas of the curriculum

Explore

How do we find out?

What's In Water?

Read aloud the introductory paragraph on Student Book page 28. As a class, brainstorm different kinds of substances that get mixed with the water that leaves children's homes. Possibilities include: dish soap, human waste, bits of food, motor oil, paint. Record children's ideas. Afterwards, ask children what they think happens to the water mixed with all these various substances that leaves their homes. (Acknowledge all reasonable responses.)

Where Water Goes

Explain to children that waste water is disposed of in one of two ways. In large communities, the water is cleaned at a place called a water treatment plant by means of filters and chemicals before it is returned to a nearby lake or river. In small or rural communities, waste water is carried from peoples' homes to septic tanks. The waste or solids in the water stay in these tanks and decay over time. The water is carried from the tank through pipes into the soil.
Ask children what they think would happen if waste water was not cleaned before it was returned to a body of water in the environment. (Look for children to realize that this water would pollute the source of water to which it was returned and harm or kill living things including themselves.)

Effects of Polluted Water

Ask children to examine the photographs on Student Book page 29 and discuss each one. Record children's responses under one of three headings: People, Other Animals, Plants. Ask:

What do you think is polluting the water in the photograph of the ship?
(Answers may vary. Look for children to realize oil leaking from the ship is polluting the water.)

How do you think the oil spill will affect people, other animals, and plants?
(Answers will vary. Possibilities include "Oil could get into birds' feathers making it impossible for them to fly." "Fish could swallow the oil and die." "Oil could cover plants and kill them.")

What do you think happened in the photograph of the seagull?
(Answers may vary. Look for children to realize the gull became covered with oil possibly after landing on an oil spill.)

What do you think will happen to the seagull?
(It will probably die because it can't fly in search of food, shelter, or protection from its enemies.)

What do you think is polluting the water in the photograph of the pipe?
(Answers may vary. Possibilities include "Waste from peoples' homes." "Chemicals from factories.")

How do you think these things will affect the plants and animals?
(Answers will vary. Possibilities include "Animals might get sick or die if they drink the water." "The water might get so dirty that underwater plants won't get enough sunshine to grow." "People might swim in the water and get sick.")

Exploration Results

Through discussion, children should realize that untreated or polluted water can affect the health of all living things.

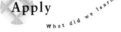

Apply

What did we learn?

Reducing Pollution

Organize children into groups to research water pollution. Brainstorm possible causes of pollution. (Possibilities include oil spills, untreated waste from homes, and chemicals from factories.) Ask children to find answers to the following questions:

What causes the pollution?

How are people, animals, and/or plants affected by the pollution?

What are people doing or what can they do to reduce or stop the pollution?

Collect books and multimedia resources about water pollution. Children could share their findings with the class by making a poster, writing a short report, or giving a presentation.
Alternatively, you could use the suggestions outlined in the Think! section and have children investigate causes of and solutions to pollution within their own homes.

Extending Learning

Invite someone from your local water works department to give a talk to the class about the processes involved in treating waste water before it is returned to the environment. As a class, brainstorm questions children would like answered. Provide the speaker with a list of these questions prior to the visit.

Struggling Learners

As your guest speaker from the water works talks, record the various steps waste water undergoes from leaving peoples' homes to returning to a lake or river. Use these notes to draw a diagram for children outlining the journey of waste water. The diagram could be a simple one consisting of a series of labelled boxes linked together by arrows. Children can help identify the steps.

Integrating Science

Language Arts: Read About Water
Read aloud *I am Water* by Jean Marzollo (Scholastic, New York, New York, 1996), a simple and powerful story about the need to use water wisely for the sake of all living things. Have children use the pattern of this story to write their own story about the need for people to use water wisely.

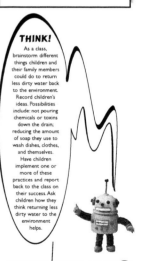

THINK!
As a class, brainstorm different things children and their family members could do to return less dirty water back to the environment. Record children's ideas. Possibilities include: not pouring chemicals or toxins down the drain; reducing the amount of soap they use to wash dishes, clothes, and themselves. Have children implement one or more of these practices and report back to the class on their success. Ask children how they think returning less dirty water to the environment helps.

Exploration Results
- description of the expected outcome of the Exploration

Extending Learning
- ideas to extend students' understanding or interest in the concept

Think!
- answers to the questions or activities to extend students' thinking about the concept

This icon indicates content related to Aboriginal peoples.

Correlation to British Columbia Curriculum

Animals Grow: Grade 2—Animal Growth and Changes

Learning Outcomes	Lessons
• classify familiar animals according to similarities and differences in appearance, behaviour, and life cycles (T1)	Throughout unit
• describe some changes that affect animals (T2)	Lessons 7, 8, 10, 14
• describe how animals are important in the lives of Aboriginal peoples in BC (T3)	Lessons 6, 13, 14
• describe ways in which animals are important to other living things and the environment (T4)	Lessons 2, 3, 4, 5, 6, 7, 8, 9, 11, 13, 14
Processes and Skills of Science	
• use their senses to interpret observations (P5)	Lessons 2, 4, 5, 6, 7, 8, 10, 11, 13
• infer the probable outcome of an event or behaviour based on observations (P6)	Lessons 2, 3, 4, 5, 8, 9, 10, 12, 14
The above processes of science learning outcomes are specific to this grade level. Since students develop ability in the various process skills throughout their school lives, any of the curriculum process skills that are addressed in a particular unit are assessed in that unit. (See the Assessment section on the first page of each lesson.)	
Attitudes	
• show respect for Aboriginal peoples and other cultures (A4)	Lessons 11, 13, 14

Interpreting Observations (P5)

This involves drawing conclusions based on observations and interpretations. It also involves making sensory comparisons and inferences using facts or observations to draw conclusions about or create explanations for events not directly observed.

Making Inferences (P6)

Guessing about the next probable event or behaviour helps the student to formulate reasonable predictions. These expected outcomes are based on a number of previous observations of the same or similar events.

The outcomes in bold are the focus for this grade

- use the five senses to make observations (P1)
- share with others information obtained by observing (P2)
- communicate their observations, experiences, and thinking in a variety of ways (P3)
- classify objects, events, and organisms (P4)
- **use their senses to interpret observations (P5)**
- **infer the probable outcome of an event or behaviour based on observations (P6)**
- ask questions that foster investigations and explorations relevant to the content (P7)
- measure objects and events (P8)
- make predictions supported by reason and relevant to the content (P9)
- use data from investigations to recognize patterns and relationships and make conclusions (P10)

- identify variables that can be changed in an experiment (P11)
- describe variables that can be tested in an experiment (P12)
- describe the steps in designing an experiment (P13)
- evaluate the fairness of a given experiment (P14)
- apply solutions to a technical problem (P15)
- test a hypothesis by planning and conducting an experiment that controls two or more variables (P16)
- create models that help to explain scientific concepts and hypotheses (P17)

Lesson Planning Guide for

Lesson	Time	Content	Materials
Lesson 1 pages 12-18 **Student Book** pages 4-5	Activate: 15-20 min Explore: 15-20 min Apply: 20-30 min	Children are encouraged to think about animals by researching and writing about specific animals.	**Activate:** Science Journals, Reproducible 1A **Explore:** large sheet of paper **Apply:** Reproducible 1B
Lesson 2 pages 19-24 **Student Book** pages 6-7	Activate: 10 min Explore: 30-45 min Apply: 10-15 min	Children learn that animals have a life cycle that involves birth, reproduction, and death.	**Activate:** pictures of animals **Explore:** **Apply:** Reproducible 2
Lesson 3 pages 25-30 **Student Book** pages 8-9	Activate: 10-15 min Explore: 45-50 min Apply: 30 min	Children discover that animals start their lives as fertilized eggs that may develop inside or outside the mother.	**Explore:** Reproducible 3A **Apply:** chicken egg, 100-W bulb, paper-towel tube, bowl; Reproducible 3B
Lesson 4 pages 31-35 **Student Book** pages 10-11	Activate: 15 min Explore: 60-80 min Apply: 30-40 min	Children learn about the larva that hatches from an egg.	**Explore:** *larvae, *food gel, twigs, plastic cups, a small paintbrush, coffee filters, elastics, magnifiers **Apply:** Reproducible 4A
Lesson 5 pages 36-41 **Student Book** pages 12-13	Activate: 10 min Explore: 20-30 min Apply: 20-30 min	Children observe how a larva becomes a pupa, the next stage in the life cycle.	**Explore:** sugar, water, cotton balls, larva houses from previous lesson **Apply:** Reproducible 5A
Lesson 6 pages 42-47 **Student Book** pages 14-15	Activate: 10-15 min Explore: 30-40 min Apply: 20-30 min	Children explore the life cycles of birds.	**Activate:** bird feathers, bird's nest (optional); modelling clay and pictures for ESL learners **Apply:** Reproducible 6A
Lesson 7 pages 48-53 **Student Book** pages 16-17	Activate: 15 min Explore: 30-45 min Apply: 30-45 min	Children explore ways animals cope with winter. Children also construct a bird feeder.	**Explore:** 1-L cardboard milk containers or plastic pop bottles, scissors, pencils or twigs, *string or yarn, sunflower seeds or other bird seed **Apply:** Reproducibles 7A and 7B
Lesson 8 pages 54-59 **Student Book** pages 18-19	Activate: 10 min Explore: 30-40 min Apply: 20 min	Children discover where animals live.	**Activate:** a small caged animal or a fish in a bowl (optional) **Apply:** Reproducible 8A
Lesson 9 pages 60-65 **Student Book** pages 20-21	Activate: 10-15 min Explore: 15-20 min Apply: 20 min	Children learn about the human life cycle.	**Activate:** a real baby and/or pictures of babies **Explore:** Reproducible 9A
Lesson 10 pages 66-70 **Student Book** pages 22-23	Activate: 10-15 min Explore: 20 min Apply: 25-30 min	Children investigate how humans change throughout the life cycle.	**Explore:** *measuring tapes; adult and baby volunteers (if possible) **Apply:** Reproducible 10A
Lesson 11 pages 71-76 **Student Book** pages 24-25	Activate: 10 min Explore: 15-20 min Apply: 20-25 min	Children discover how humans need food to grow and remain healthy.	**Explore:** pita bread, green pepper, tomato slices, cheese slices, pepperoni, tofu cubes; bowls, plates, napkins (not disposable); a knife **Apply:** Reproducibles 11A and 11B

* Items included in the Equipment Pack.

Animals Grow

Lesson	Time	Content	Materials
Lesson 12 pages 77-81 **Student Book** pages 26-27	Activate: 5-10 min Explore: 20-25 min Apply: 25-30 min	Children learn what makes for a healthy lifestyle.	**Activate:** pictures of people being active (e.g., playing sports, doing housework, or gardening) **Apply:** Reproducible 12
Lesson 13 pages 82-91 **Student Book** pages 28-29	Activate: 10-15 min Explore: 30-35 min Apply: 25-30 min	Children investigate how humans affect other animals.	**Explore:** Reproducible 13A **Apply:** Reproducibles 13B and 13C
Lesson 14 pages 92-99 **Student Book** pages 30-31	Activate: 10-15 min Explore: 35-40 min Apply: 35-40 min	Children compare the life cycles of different animals.	**Apply:** Reproducibles 14A and 14B

* Items included in the Equipment Pack.

Additional Resources for Teachers and Students

Websites

Fort Nelson Aboriginal Project has lots of highly accessible information about the relationship of Aboriginal peoples with plants, animals, and the environment. The site includes sample Cree and Slavey translations of some English words. http://rla.sd81.bc.ca/%7Efnap/fnaptoc.html

The Earthlife Net has information on insects, birds, and mammals. http://www.earthlifenet/

Monarch Watch and **Journey North** both have information about the monarch's migration as well as opportunities to become involved.
http://www.monarchwatch.org/
http://www.learner.org/jnorth

Canadian Nature Federation has information and programs to involve people in protecting animals.
http://www.cnf.ca/

Endangered Species and Ecosystems in British Columbia has information on endangered species and many good links to other sites.
http://srmwww.gov.bc.ca/atrisk/

Royal BC Museum is also a good site for information about endangered species in BC.
http://rbcm1.rbcm.gov.bc.ca/end_species/index_es.html/es_plans/gr2-3.html

Books

Watch Them Grow by Linda Martin (DK Publishing, 1994)

Life Cycles (Everyday Life of Animals) by Ivan Stalio, Marco Ferrari, and Fulvio Cerfolli (Raintree/Steck Vaughn, 1998)

Animal Journeys: Life Cycles and Migrations (Animals in the Wild) by Susanne Riha (Blackbirch, 1999)

All Kinds of Animals by Rosie McCormick (Kingfisher Books, 1997)

What is a Life Cycle (The Science of Living Things) by Bobbie Kalman, Jacqueline Languille (Crabtree, 1998)

The Very Last First Time by Jan Andrews and Ian Wallace III (Groundwood, 1985)

Sea Turtle by Gail Gibbons (Holiday House, 1995)

Keepers of the Animals: Native Stories and Wildlife Activities for Children, Michael Cuduto. (Fifth House, 1991)

Little Water and the Gift of the Animals, C.J. Taylor. (Tundra Books, 1992)

How Food Was Given, Okanagan Tribal Council. (Theytus Books, 1991)

Eagle Feather—An Honour, Ferguson Plain. (Pemmican, 1989)

Haida Art, Dawn Adams. (Wedge, 1983)

Crests of the Haida, Pearle Pearson with J. White (Wedge)

West Coast Rhymes, Jenny Nelson. (Gage, 1993)

Coyote as the Sun and Other Stories, Secwepemc Cultural Education Society, 1993.

How Do Animals Compare?

Student Book pages 4-5

In this lesson: Children are encouraged to think about animals by researching and writing about specific animals.

Outcomes

Children will have opportunities to:
- classify familiar animals according to similarities and differences in appearance, behaviour, and life cycles (T1)
- use the five senses to make observations (P1)
- share with others information obtained by observing (P2)
- communicate their observations, experiences, and thinking in a variety of ways (P3)
- classify objects, events, and organisms (P4)

Assessment

- Baseline Tasks: To assess children's recollections from Grade 1 as to what constitutes an animal, have them complete Reproducible 1A, *Find the Animals* on page 17 before they start this lesson. They should be able to recognize that both conditions have to be met in order for something to be defined as an animal. A plant and a garment on a clothesline both show indications of motion, but neither can choose to move, as animals can. (T1, P1, P4) Ask children to list in their Science Journals what things all animals have in common and how animals are different. At the end of the unit, have children review and revise their lists.
- Review children's charts and paragraphs from the Exploration. You should be able to tell from these whether children have understood some fundamental concepts about animal comparisons. (T1, P1, P3)
- At the end of the Exploration, listen to the children comparing the animals they have researched. Ask:

How are all animals the same? (They breathe, eat, move, rest, grow, and are able to reproduce.)

How are they different? (How they look, what they eat, how they have babies, where they live)

Do all animals need food? (yes)

Can all animals run? (no)

In what types of places do animals live? (in places where they can find the things they need to live) (T1, P1, P2, P4)

Getting Organized

Materials: large sheet of paper to make a chart; Science Journals; copies of Reproducible 1A: *Find the Animals* on page 17; Reproducible 1B: *How Do Animals Eat?* on page 18

Suggested Grouping: class, individual, small groups

Suggested Time: Activate 10–15 min; Explore 25–30, plus time for library research; Apply 10–15 min

Advance Preparation: Prepare Science Journals for students.

Animal Centre

You may already have an animal that children can observe and help care for in the classroom. Consider developing an Animal Centre where children can observe different animals throughout the unit and where they can place pictures of animals in which they develop a special interest as the unit develops. You might add an aquarium, or if a full-sized aquarium isn't possible, a bowl of goldfish. If you can obtain one, an ant farm would be fascinating for the children to observe. Any observation of animals would probably lead to many questions that you could encourage the children to explore. (Children might ask questions such as, What do the animals do? Do they always behave in the same way? Do they have routines that they follow? Are all of the ants the same size? If there's a size difference, is there a reason? Allow the children some time to work in groups to develop ways to explore some of these questions. Encourage them to carry out their explorations, if at all feasible.)

If the children have any pets that are appropriate for classroom observation (a rabbit, a hamster, a gerbil, for example, set a time when they might bring the animal in for a day or two so that it can be observed by everyone).

Lesson Vocabulary

animal: a living thing that is not a plant and can move about freely.

habitat: the place where an animal lives.

reproduce: Animals reproduce when they make babies.

Content Background

Over 2000 years ago, the Greek philosopher Aristotle began classifying living things according to whether they were plant or animal. The Swedish botanist Linnaeus developed a new system in the mid-1700s. Since then, between 1.5 million and 1.75 million species have been identified. These include plants, animals, fungi, protists, and monera.

Movement is one feature of animals. Unlike plants, most animals have developed muscles that enable them to move from place to place. How animals eat, grow, and reproduce relates to their motility, or ability to move. Scientifically, it is not really accurate to differentiate between plants and animals on the basis of their ability to move. Not all animals can move. However, this is a useful and appropriate dichotomy for children at this level.

When animals grow, almost all parts of their bodies enlarge. Although animals vary in appearance, all animals conform to about six basic body models. These models are determined during the embryonic phase, before the animal is born or hatched.

The most well-known classes of animals include mammals, reptiles, amphibians, birds, fish, and insects.

CURIOSITY PLACE

There are more kinds of insects than there are any other kind of animal.

Lesson 1: How Do Animals Compare?

Activate

What do we want to know? What do we know?

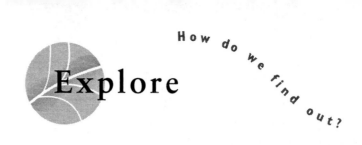

Explore

How do we find out?

Distribute or have students make Science Journals. Talk to them about the sorts of things they will be including in their journal—any questions they have, their observations, results of explorations. They can draw pictures, write, make charts, and so on in their journals. Model a journal entry for students on the board.

Help children to draw on their personal experience of animals. Have them describe pets or farm animals they have known. Quiz them about wild animals seen at the zoo or in their natural setting. Ask:

How are all animals the same?
(They breathe, eat, move, rest, grow, are able to reproduce, and excrete.)

How are they different?

Record the correct answers on the board. If children bring up the fact that all animals "go to the bathroom," explain that animals get rid of food they can't use and that this process is called excretion. Now prompt the children to become more specific in their descriptions. Ask:

How do these animals look?

What do these animals eat?

Where do these animals live?

Preconceptions

Children may have trouble grasping how animals differ from other living things. Emphasizing that animals can move, whereas plants generally cannot, will help children with the concept of animal.

Read the paragraph on page 4. Ask children if they can name the animals shown on the world map and their different habitats. Explain the meaning of "habitat," and have the children give examples of animals that live in their local habitat.

Explain to the children that the Exploration below will help them to learn about how animals are both the same and different.

Exploration

Compare two animals.

1. Have the class prepare three questions about animals. Make sure that the questions reflect some of the broad concepts in the Student Book (for example, diet, size, movement, body covering, raising of young, habitat). The questions should apply to all the animals chosen by the children. Record the questions on a chart on a large sheet of paper.

2. Ask each child to choose two animals to research. List all of the animals chosen on the class chart. Have the children record the three questions and their two animals in their Science Journal. Arrange to visit the library so the children can find resource materials for their research. Encourage them to use a variety of media including the Internet and CD-ROMs. The children can record information in point form in their Science Journal chart.

3. Ask the children to rewrite their information in paragraphs or share what they learned with the class orally. How do the animals compare? Record the information on the class chart. Divide the children into small groups to compare animals using their reports.

Apply

What did we learn?

Troubleshooting

Create a model chart that the children can copy into their Science Journal. Show the questions running horizontally along the top of the page; the names of animals to be researched should then be listed vertically along the left margin of the page. Create a grid of empty squares, where the answers are to be recorded.

Animal	Where Does It Live?	What Does It Eat?	What Type of Body Covering Does It Have?

Exploration Results

Through discussion, research, and writing, children should discover that all animals have some common characteristics, but that they also all differ. Depending on the questions selected by the class, children will recognize differences in animals' appearance, movement, diet, growth, reproduction, or habitat.

Global Perspectives

Humans distinguish between domestic animals (animals that are dependent on humans to meet their needs) and wild animals (animals that live in their natural environment). Of course, all animals were once wild, yet the tradition of domesticating animals is very old. It dates back at least 10 000 years. Even today, animals that are considered wild in some cultures are domesticated in others. In China, cormorants are kept as pets, but in North America they are considered wild.

Review the information on the class chart. Ask:

Which animals are similar and which are different?

Go through all three of the class questions. Then ask:

Which animals are alike in some ways and different in others?

Which animals are alike according to all three questions?

Which animals are different according to all three questions?

Make a class chart to graph this information.

THINK!
Different animals can crack, tear, rip, slurp, or strangle their food. Some animals chew their food while others swallow it whole.

Apply

What did we learn?

Extending Learning

Compare ways that animals find and eat their food. You might want to read *Amazing Mouths & Menus* by Mary Blocksma (Prentice-Hall, 1986) to the class.

In their Science Journals, have the children draw a picture of the way one of the animals they studied finds and eats its food.

Now distribute Reproducible 1B: *How Do Animals Eat?* (Answers: raccoon-clam; snake-mouse; lion-impala; aardvark-ants; cow-grass) Ask the children to match the five animals with the food they eat. Discuss how they knew. Ask:

What other ways do animals eat?

Encourage children to find out about a variety of other animals and report back to the class.

Integrating Science

Art: Draw a Picture
Have children draw and colour one of the animals they researched. In the drawing, children should show as many things as possible about the animal (for example, its appearance, habitat, food).

Language Arts: Write a Play
As a class, choose two of the animals researched and pretend they are meeting for the first time. Ask the children to help you write a short play or sketch about the introduction of the animals. In the play, have the animals discover their similarities and differences. Once the play is complete, you could ask two volunteers to act out the roles of the animals for the class.

Alternatively, the children could make hand puppets and act out the meeting of two animals in a puppet theatre.

Name ______________________ Date ______________________

Reproducible 1A

Find the Animals

Look at the following pictures. Use a check mark to answer the questions. At the bottom of the page write two things that tell you that something is an animal.

	Yes	No
1. Is it alive?	___	___
Can it decide to move?	___	___
Is it an animal?	___	___
2. Is it alive?	___	___
Can it decide to move?	___	___
Is it an animal?	___	___
3. Is it alive?	___	___
Can it decide to move?	___	___
Is it an animal?	___	___
4. Is it alive?	___	___
Can it decide to move?	___	___
Is it an animal?	___	___
5. Is it alive?	___	___
Can it decide to move?	___	___
Is it an animal?	___	___
6. Is it alive?	___	___
Can it decide to move?	___	___
Is it an animal?	___	___

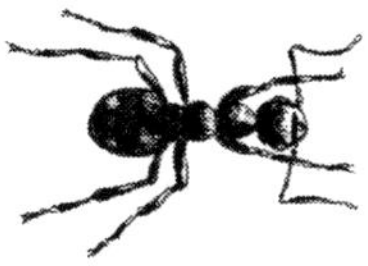

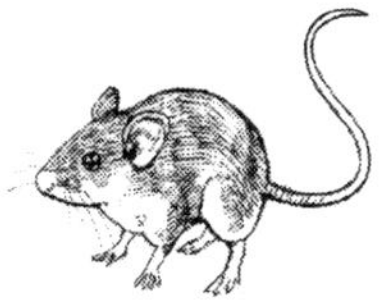

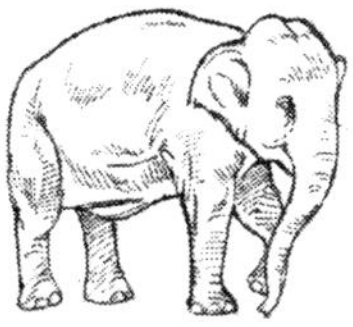

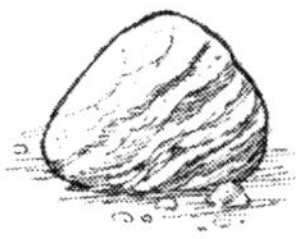

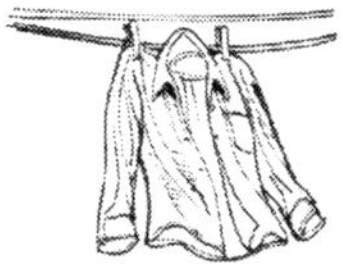

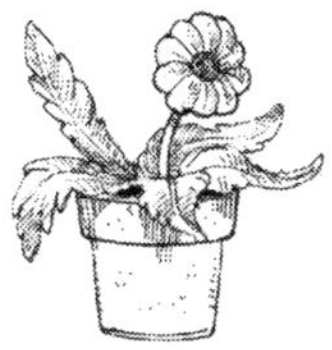

I know something is an animal because ______________________

____

____

How Do Animals Eat?

Draw a line to match each animal with the food it eats.
How do you know what belongs together?

What Is a Life Cycle?

Student Book pages 6–7

In this lesson: Children learn that animals have a life cycle that involves birth, reproduction, and death.

Outcomes

Children will have opportunities to:
- classify familiar animals according to similarities and differences in appearance, behaviour, and life cycles (T1)
- describe ways in which animals are important to other living things and the environment (T4)
- use the five senses to make observations (P1)
- communicate their observations, experiences, and thinking in a variety of ways (P3)
- use their senses to interpret observations (P5)
- infer the probable outcome of an event or behaviour based on observations (P6)

Assessment

- Question children to find out whether they understand there are different types of animals. Ask: **Can you define a mammal? Name one. Is a snake a mammal? Why not? Are a fish and an insect the same kind of animal? Why not?** (T1, P6)
- Review the children's Science Journal drawings from the Exploration. The drawings should show the animal changing throughout the life cycle. Constant traits should also be visible. (T1, T4, P1, P3, P6)
- Children's responses in the Activate will help you to assess their ability to infer from their observations. (P5, P6)

Getting Organized

Materials: pictures of animals; copies of Reproducible 2: *How Many Baby Animals?* on pages 23-24.

Suggested Grouping: individual

Time Required: Activate 10 min; Explore 20 min plus out-of-class time; Apply 20 min

Advance Preparation: Arrange for a few different pets to visit the classroom. Avoid pets that are likely to upset any of the children.

Safety: Check whether any of the children are allergic to specific animals or their dander prior to pet visits. Make sure that children take care during and wash their hands following the handling of pets.

Lesson Vocabulary

camouflage: An animal camouflages itself by blending in with its surroundings. Some plants and animals live in habitats whose colour closely matches their own. Others can change their colour.

life cycle: all the changes a plant or an animal goes through between its birth and death. Every living animal has a life cycle.

mammal: an animal that usually has fur or hair on its body and nurses its young with milk. Almost all mammals are born alive instead of hatching from eggs. Humans, dogs, cows, and mice are examples of mammals.

trait: a feature or characteristic that helps to identify an animal (for example, scaly body covering).

Activate

Content Background

Life cycles range from the very simple to the complex. A very simple animal may reproduce asexually, by pinching or budding off a part of itself. Usually the bud stays attached to the original animal. Sexual reproduction in higher animals involves an egg that must be fertilized (see Lesson 3).

To grow well and reach maturity, young animals need a favourable environment with adequate food. Some animals—mammals in particular—also need parental care.

In a complex life cycle, the juvenile animal may look very different from the adult animal. Consider a salamander. Like most amphibians, it has a juvenile phase in water, when it breathes through gills. Later, it turns into a sexually mature animal that breathes air.

Animals with complex life cycles benefit from living in two different environments, each with its own food supply. One environment may also offer greater safety at the juvenile stage. For instance, many salamander larvae hatch in pools in the spring. The absence of fish in these temporary pools lessens danger to the salamander eggs and larvae.

ESL Learners

Show the children the pictures of the animal at different stages of its life cycle. Have the children draw those characteristics that stay the same and those that change throughout the life cycle. Discuss the characteristics with the children as they point them out.

Bring in pictures of an animal showing how it looked when it was just born, partially grown, and fully mature. Choose an animal that looks somewhat different at each stage. Ask:

How many kinds of animals are in these pictures?

How do you know?

Have the children explain their responses. Encourage them to compare the pictures by pointing out constant and changing traits. Ask:

What parts of the animal's body grow a lot?

Do some parts of the animal's body stay the same all its life?

Do all animals change as much as this one as they grow and get older?

Summarize the correct conclusions by writing them on the board.

Preconceptions

Understandably, some children may believe that an immature animal and a mature animal that look very different cannot belong to the same life cycle. For instance, they might think that a tadpole and a frog are not the same animal. One purpose of this lesson is to emphasize the development of the animal throughout the life cycle.

Read page 6 of the Student Book. Then reinforce the concept of life cycle by discussing the definition on pages 32-33.

The Exploration will be done outside of the classroom in the children's own time. Discuss the steps of the Exploration so that the children understand what to do.

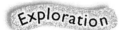

Illustrate changes.

1. Children will need to locate a pet. The pet might be their own, a neighbour's, a friend's, or a relative's. If the children cannot find a pet, perhaps there is one in another class in the school. The children should then draw the pet in their Science Journal. Encourage the children to observe the animal closely and to record as much detail as possible. Remind children to exercise caution around the pet they choose.

2. Once the children have drawn the pet, have them ask the pet owner about how the animal looked at an earlier stage and how it will look at a later stage. Remind the children to ask which traits of the animal have stayed the same and which have changed.

3. The children should use the information to make two more drawings in their Science Journal.

Exploration Results

Children should discover that most animals progress through a life cycle that includes birth, reproduction, and death. Some traits characterize an animal throughout its life cycle, while other traits change as the animal grows and matures.

Have the children share the drawings in their Science Journal and discuss them. If possible, have several pets visit the class, particularly ones with different life cycles (for example, birds, reptiles, mammals, insects). Make sure the children treat the pets with respect. Encourage the children to compare the life cycles of similar animals with those of different animals.

Look at the pets in the illustration on page 7 of the Student Book. Explain that they are both mammals. Mammals are born alive. Their bodies are usually covered with hair or fur. They drink milk from their mothers. This means that they need at least one parent to care for them after they are born.

Then distribute Reproducible 2: *How Many Baby Animals?* Have the children cut out the pictures and sort them into adults and babies. Then ask the children to match the adults with their own babies.
Ask:

How do animals stay the same as they grow?

How do they change?

Discuss how animals stay the same as they grow. For example, the number of legs and skin covering (except with some insects and amphibians) are constant traits. Then discuss how animals change. Young animals usually get bigger, heavier, and stronger as they grow.

Troubleshooting

Make sure the children select a pet that the owner has known through different stages of the life cycle or has considerable knowledge about. Otherwise, the children will have trouble producing the final two drawings.

Apply

What did we learn?

Extending Learning

Make a list of baby animals that look the same and those that look different from their parents. Ask students why they think some young animals are a different colour than their parents. Explain that colours and patterns can protect animals as they hide. Explain that blending in with the surroundings is called "camouflage." Children can draw or find pictures of the animals in their natural habitat.

You may wish to take the children to visit a local pet store, veterinarian, farm, or zoo to observe baby animals. If possible, encourage the children to compare the offspring to their parents. Work with children to develop a list of questions ahead of time about animal growth. With the class, prepare a poster-sized set of answers to display in the classroom.

CURIOSITY PLACE

Rats and mice can have as many as 12 babies at a time. Cats usually have between three and five babies in a litter, while dogs have between four and eight babies at a time. Animals like cows and deer usually have just one baby at a time.

THINK!

Yes! Most baby animals do look like their parents in many ways.

Integrating Science

Language Arts: Read a Book
Share books about animals, their babies, and life cycles with students. Some suggestions include:

Freedman, Russell. *Farm Babies*. New York: Holiday House, 1981.

Gibbons, Gail. *Frogs*. New York: Holiday House, 1993.

Kalman, Bobbie. *Animal Babies*. Toronto: Crabtree Press, 1987.

Ling, Mary. *Butterfly*. Richmond Hill: Scholastic Canada, 1992.

Trevor, Terry & Margaret Linton. *The Life Cycle of an Ant*. Hove, England: Wayland, 1987.

Williams, John. *The Life Cycle of a Frog*. Hove, England: Wayland, 1987.

Social Studies: Write a Comparison
As a class, discuss different animal families. Think about how long the young remain with the parent or parents and how many young there are. Consider how the parents care for and train their young. Then ask children how these compare with human families. Emphasize that with humans, as with many animals, there are many kinds of families. You could ask the children to write down their comparisons.

How Many Baby Animals?

Cut out these animals.
Sort them into adults and babies.
Then match the baby with its parent.

Name _____ Date _____

How Many Baby Animals? (continued)

What Is Inside an Egg?

Student Book pages 8–9

In this lesson: Children discover that animals start their lives as fertilized eggs that may develop inside or outside the mother.

Outcomes

Children will have opportunities to:
- classify familiar animals according to similarities and differences in appearance, behaviour, and life cycles (T1)
- describe ways in which animals are important to other living things and the environment (T4)
- use the five senses to make observations (P1)
- share with others information obtained by observing (P2)
- classify objects, events, and organisms (P4)
- infer the probable outcome of an event or behaviour based on observations (P6)

Assessment

- Children's responses in the Activate and Extending Learning will help you to assess their ability to make inferences. (P6)
- Children's answers and comments in Apply and Extending Learning will reveal whether they understand that some animals hatch from eggs and others are born live. They will demonstrate what they know about the advantages or disadvantages of each system and the implications for parent behaviour. (T1, T4, P1, P2, P4, P6)
- Collect Reproducible 3A and check each child's drawings. They will show whether the children understand how animals use their environment. (T4)

Getting Organized

Materials: Reproducible 3A: *Where Do Reptiles Get Warm?* on page 29, and Reproducible 3B: *What Is Inside an Egg?* on page 30; a chicken egg, a lamp with a 100-W light bulb, a paper-towel tube, a bowl

Suggested Grouping: class, individual, small groups

Time Required: Activate 10–15 min; Explore 20–25 min; Apply 20–30 min

Advance Preparation: Get a chicken egg, a paper-towel tube, a 100-W lamp, and a bowl.

Safety: Make sure children do not handle the raw egg. If any child touches the raw egg, warn the child to keep the egg away from his or her mouth, and have the child wash up immediately.

Lesson Vocabulary

bask: A basking animal lies in the Sun.

egg: cells produced by female animals. Eggs can be fertilized to produce new life.

fertilize: A cell from a male animal joins onto an egg to fertilize it. A fertilized egg can produce a new life.

reptile: an animal that has dry skin made up of scales or plates and is cold-blooded. Most female reptiles lay eggs. Snakes, lizards, and turtles are examples of reptiles.

offspring: the progeny or product of a plant or animal

Activate

What do we know? What do we want to know?

Content Background

Of all the many types of cells in an animal's body, an egg is the largest in the female, and the sperm is one of the smallest in the male. Sperm cells contain half the male's genetic material, and unfertilized eggs contain half the female's genetic material. For life to develop, the sperm and the egg must unite.

Fertilization may occur inside or outside the female's body. Some animals, such as frogs and certain fish, use external fertilizations. Inside the egg is nourishment and developmental information that is triggered into action by the sperm.

The sizes, shapes, and textures of eggs vary from species to species. Birds have hard-shelled eggs; one end of the egg is almost always narrower than the other—sometimes extremely so—which prevents the egg from rolling away easily. Reptile eggs are leathery-shelled and full of water and yolk. The eggs of insects and water-dwelling animals are usually very small and jelly-like.

Nearly all mammalian eggs develop inside the mother; they have no shell and receive nourishment though a protective organ inside the uterus called the placenta. When a baby hatches or is born alive, the fertilized egg has grown from an embryo into an organism that can mature and survive in a particular environment.

Encourage children to begin by thinking about animals that lay eggs. Bird eggs may be the most familiar. Ask:

What do eggs look like?

Where are they found?

How do female or male animals care for their eggs?

What do you think would happen if the animal didn't sit on the eggs? Why?

Record the answers on the board. Encourage children to articulate that sitting on eggs keeps them warm and that if they are not kept warm, their contents will die. Then encourage the children to reflect on animals that are not listed. Have them name animals that give birth to live young. Pets, such as cats, may come to mind. Ask:

Are there some animals that do not lay eggs?

Do these animals look different from animals that lay eggs? How?

Where do female animals give birth to live young?

How do female or male animals care for live young?

Preconceptions

Children may find it hard to grasp why animals that differ in appearance and behaviour come under the same broad category of "mammal" or "reptile." This lesson can help them understand that whether an egg develops inside or outside a mother's body can help in classifying animals.

Explore

Read page 8 of the Student Book. Have the children recall that most animals born alive are mammals. Then encourage the children to name some animals that hatch from eggs. Ask:

Have you seen an animal hatch from an egg? How did it happen?

Now show children the photo of the turtle hatching, on page 8. Explain that the turtle is not a mammal, but a reptile. Introduce the definition of "reptile."

Explain that reptiles are cold-blooded (i.e., their body temperature is affected by the environment outside them). Mammals may feel cold on a winter day, but their body temperature does not change. To stay warm on a cold spring day, reptiles find a sunny place to bask.

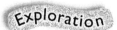

Get to know reptiles.

1. Have the children choose three reptiles (such as turtles, snakes, lizards, iguanas, geckos, tortoises, crocodiles or alligators). Record the reptiles' names on the board. Make sure all of the children know what these reptiles look like. They will need to draw them in the next step.
2. Discuss what kinds of places reptiles might use to sun themselves (rocks, by a building, sidewalk, beach, river bank). Now hand out Reproducible 3A: *Where Do Reptiles Get Warm?* (Reptiles would sun themselves on a rock, a log, a concrete sidewalk)

Troubleshooting

Make sure children understand that reptiles are not the only animals that lay eggs. Otherwise, children may suggest birds or fish when you ask them to name three reptiles.

Exploration Results

Children should understand that animals fall into different categories (for example, mammals, reptiles, amphibians, birds, fish). Some animals give birth to live young and others lay eggs. Animals use their environment to satisfy their needs.

Discuss the photographs on page 9 with the children. Ask if kittens hatch out of eggs like the baby duck. Ask what we call the mother of the kittens, what we call the mother of the tadpoles, and what is another word for baby duck?

CURIOSITY PLACE

The eggs of a human, an elephant, a whale, and a mouse are about the same size.

Gifted Children

Have gifted children discuss how and why scientists classify animals into groups, such as mammals and reptiles. Ask:

How do scientists decide to which group an animal belongs?

How might classifying animals help scientists with their research?

You will be discussing this idea with the entire class in Lesson 14. If the class has difficulty, gifted children may be able to help at that point by presenting their ideas.

Apply

What did we learn?

Discuss how some animals use their environment to meet their needs. Explain that some animals, such as birds, gather twigs and grass to make nests. Other animals, such as turtles, dig a hole in the earth.

Explain how some animals care for their eggs. Some birds sit on their eggs to keep them warm and protect them. Other animals, like turtles, lay their eggs in a hole, cover the hole with soil, and leave their young to hatch and take care of themselves.

To help answer, "Think! Why do birds' eggs have shells?", bring in a chicken egg. Let the children handle it gently. Discuss the shape of the egg and let the children try to roll it.

Hold the egg close to a lit 100-W bulb and place one end of a paper-towel tube against it. Let children take turns looking through the other end of the tube to view the illuminated yolk mass.

Crack the egg into a bowl and ask the children what they see. Explain that the yolk is part of the egg that would have grown into a chicken if the egg had been fertilized. Reassure the children that humans eat only unfertilized eggs. (A fertilized egg will have a red dot inside.) Show the children how the yolk provides food for the unborn chick while it is growing inside the egg. The white (albumen) is for shockproofing and moisture. Describe how a hen sits on the egg to keep it at the right temperature and protect it from danger.

Extending Learning

Ask children how they think a creature that is developing inside an egg "knows" when it is time to come out of the shell. How might they find out?

Talk about how creatures developing inside eggs get their food. Ask children how young animals born alive are kept safe, since they do not have shells. Does this mean their parents must care for them?

Give out Reproducible 3B: *What Is Inside an Egg?*

Integrating Science

Social Studies: Make a Map

Explain to children that the same animal can sometimes live in different environments. To illustrate, show some pictures (for example, a blue jay in a garden in Toronto and in the woods of Virginia). Then ask each child to choose one wild animal found in Canada and to research its other habitats throughout North America. This is a good opportunity for some computer research. Distribute a basic outline map of North America, and have children mark the habitats of their animal. Children can present their findings to the class.

Language Arts: Write a List Poem

As a class, choose a few animals that hatch from eggs. Ask the students to find words that describe how these animals look, feel, and sound. Then divide the class into smaller groups. Using the listed words, each group should write a poem about one of the animals.

THINK!
Birds' eggs have shells to keep the developing bird inside safe.

Where Do Reptiles Get Warm?

Circle the three places where reptiles go to get warm.
In the empty boxes, draw these three places.
Then draw a different reptile in each box.

What Is Inside an Egg?

Cut out the animals.
Paste them where they belong.

Hatch from Eggs	Born Alive

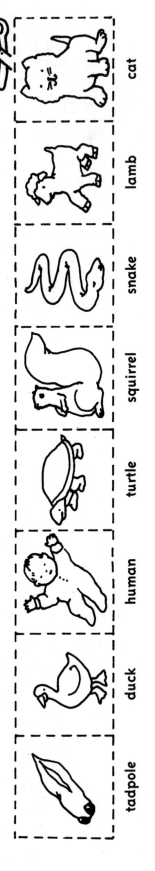

cat

lamb

snake

squirrel

turtle

human

duck

tadpole

What Is a Larva?

Student Book pages 10–11

In this lesson: Children learn about the larva that hatches from an egg.

Important: If you hatch a butterfly, it should be done in the spring.

Outcomes

Children will have opportunities to:
- describe ways in which animals are important to other living things and the environment (T4)
- communicate observations, experiences, and thinking in a variety of ways (P3)
- use their senses to interpret observations (P5)
- infer the probable outcome of an event or behaviour based on observations (P6)
- ask questions that foster investigations and explorations relevant to the content (P7)

Also T1, P1, P2, P4

Assessment

- The discussion during the introduction to the Exploration will help you to assess the children's ability to make inferences and ask questions that lend themselves to further investigation. (P6, P7)
- Review the children's drawings and notes from the Exploration. The journals should show the development of the larvae. (T1, T4, P1, P2, P3, P4, P5)
- Hand out Reproducible 4B: *What Does the Larva Eat?* on page 35. The children's answers will show whether they understood the basic concept of a larva. (T1, P6)

Getting Organized

Materials: Reproducible 4A: *What Is a Larva?* on page 34 and Reproducible 4B: *What Does the Larva Eat?* on page 35; larvae, food gel, twigs, plastic cups, a small paintbrush, coffee filters, elastics, a magnifier

Suggested Grouping: class, individuals

Time Required: Activate 5–10 min; Explore 25–30 min first day, plus 10 min over three days; Apply 25–30 min

Advance Preparation: Order larvae 4–6 weeks ahead.

Safety: Make sure children do not taste the food gel.

Lesson Vocabulary

larva: When an insect hatches from its egg, it is a larva. Sometimes a larva becomes a pupa and hatches again before it resembles its parents.

Content Background

Many insects, fish, and amphibians go through metamorphosis—a dramatic change of form—as they develop.

A caterpillar—the larva of a butterfly—hatches from an egg and begins to eat leaves voraciously. As it grows, the larva moults or sheds its unstretchable skin. As the caterpillar eats and eats and grows and grows, it moults a half dozen or so times.

Eventually, the caterpillar stops eating, finds a twig, and spins a pad of silk from which it hangs upside down. A few days later, it moults again to reveal itself as a pupa enclosed in the hard case of its chrysalis, or cocoon.

Inside the chrysalis, the pupa slowly reorganizes its body into its adult form, the butterfly. One or two weeks later the butterfly emerges, so tired from shedding its cocoon that it rests and pumps blood into its wings. After the wings have dried, the insect can fly.

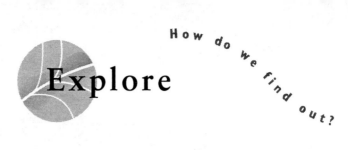

Ask children to solve this riddle: What is woolly and soft, is just centimetres long, is round and found on leaves and on the ground?

They should be able to guess the answer is a caterpillar, which children sometimes call a woolly bear.

Ask children if they have ever seen caterpillars. Where did they see them? How did they move? What did they eat?

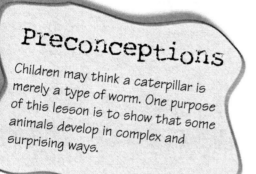

Preconceptions

Children may think a caterpillar is merely a type of worm. One purpose of this lesson is to show that some animals develop in complex and surprising ways.

ESL Learners

Show children pictures of caterpillars. Use simple words and pictures to explain that the caterpillar is a baby insect and to describe the way larvae eat and change.

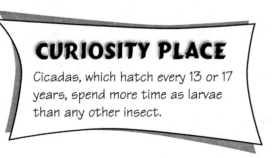

CURIOSITY PLACE

Cicadas, which hatch every 13 or 17 years, spend more time as larvae than any other insect.

Read page 10 of the Student Book. Ask:

How do caterpillars change as they grow?

Do they get bigger?

Do they change form? How could you find out?

Encourage children to tell you how they might set up an experiment like the one they will do in this lesson.

Exploration

Build a larva house.

Note: These instructions are for the larvae of the painted lady butterfly. You can also use brine shrimp or mealworm larvae instead. All will have to be preordered. If you are using butterfly larvae, do this activity in spring so that the butterfly can be released.

1. Have the materials ready (larvae, food gel, twigs, plastic cups, a small paint brush, coffee filters, elastics, magnifiers) laid out on a large surface around which the children can gather. Ask the children to assist you by handing over the twigs, paintbrush, coffee filters, and elastics. Do not allow the children to handle the larvae or the gel.

   Explain what you are doing. Divide the food gel and twigs among the plastic cups. Pack the food gel at the bottom of each cup.

2. Show the children the larvae. Ask them to observe the larvae with a magnifier and note their different traits. They should then draw the larvae in their Science Journals.

   Now put the larvae into the plastic cups. Take care in separating the larvae. Each cup can hold up to six larvae. Over the lip of each cup, place a coffee filter and secure it with an elastic band. The coffee filter allows air into the cup, and it also serves as a surface to which the larvae can attach themselves.

Apply

What did we learn?

3. Encourage the children to observe the larvae whenever they can over the next few days. Suggest that they focus on the life processes of the larvae: eating, breathing, movement, and rest patterns. Have them record their observations in their Science Journals.

Troubleshooting

So as to not damage the larvae, use the small paintbrush to separate them and guide them into their respective cups. Explain to the children that once the larvae are no longer protected by their eggshell, they are vulnerable and can easily be hurt.

Exploration Results

Through drawing and writing in their Science Journal, children should become familiar with the traits, life processes, and development of the larvae.

Global Perspectives

Many of the Native Peoples of the Amazon, such as the Yanomamo, have larvae as part of their diet because they are easy to find and rich in protein. The Tasaday of the Philippines eat grubs, which are a worm-like larvae.

THINK!
The ladybug, the wood louse, the pupa, the butterfly, and the snake are not larvae.

In groups, ask children to discuss what they observed. You can help their discussion by asking questions such as:

> Did the larvae change in any way? How?
>
> Did they eat a lot or a little?
>
> Could you see the larvae breathing?
>
> Did the larvae move around or did they rest a lot?
>
> Why did we put food into the larvae house?
>
> Did some larvae grow faster than others? Why might this be?

Explain to the children that the larvae depend on food for energy, which they need to live and grow. Hand out Reproducible 4B: *What Does the Larva Eat?* (Answer: leaves)

Extending Learning

Supply the children with modelling clay and a tree branch. Challenge them to construct a model to help explain how a larva feeds.

Integrating Science

Art: Make a Collage
As a class, recall the colours, patterns, shapes, and textures of the larvae you have studied. Then have each child create a collage using these details as an inspiration.

More Science: Discuss and Draw
Now the children know what and how larvae eat, but who eats larvae? Some humans do (for example, the Amazon tribe of the Yanomamo) and so do some animals (for example, birds). Through some examples, introduce the idea of the food chain. Then have the children draw a larva eating its food and a larger animal eating the larva.

Name _____ Date _____

What Is a Larva?

Draw a larva.

What words describe a larva?

_____

_____

_____

_____

What Does the Larva Eat?

Circle the food the larva will eat. Now cut out
the larva food and paste it into the jar.
What will happen to the larva if it has no food?

seeds

leaves

rocks

insects

What Is a Pupa?

Student Book pages 12–13

In this lesson: Children observe how a larva becomes a pupa, the next stage in the life cycle.

Outcomes

Children will have opportunities to:
- describe ways in which animals are important to other living things and the environment (T4)
- use their senses to interpret observations (P5)
- infer the probable outcome of an event or behaviour based on observations (P6)
- make predictions, supported by reasons and relevant to the content (P9)

Also T1, P1, P2, P3, P4

Assessment

- Collect the Science Journals and review the children's notes and drawings from the Exploration. (T1, T4, P1, P2, P3, P4, P6, P9)
- Hand out Reproducible 5B: *What Is a Pupa?* on page 41. (Answers: 1. pupa 2. larva 3. egg 4. butterfly) (T1, P6)
- Take note of students' answers during the Activate discussion. Are they aware of the needs of the larvae and pupa? (P5, P6)

Getting Organized

Materials: Reproducible 5A: *What Is an Insect?* on page 40 and Reproducible 5B: *What Is a Pupa?* on page 41; sugar, water, cotton balls, larva houses from previous lesson

Suggested Grouping: class, small groups (for preparing food), individual

Time Required: Activate 10–15 min; Explore 40 min over a number of days; Apply 25–30 min

Advance Preparation: none

Safety: Accompany the children outside for the release of the butterflies.

Lesson Vocabulary

cocoon: a layer of silky threads made by some animals to protect themselves or their eggs.

insect: a small animal that usually goes through several stages before becoming an adult. The adult has six legs, three main body parts (head, thorax, and abdomen), two antennae, and usually one or two pairs of wings. An insect has an exoskeleton (its hard outer shell-like covering) that provides protection.

pupa: a stage in an insect's life cycle. When the larva stops eating and forms a case or cocoon, it becomes a pupa and changes into an adult.

Activate

Content Background

Though the pupa appears inert inside its chrysalis, or cocoon, it is actively changing into its adult stage—the butterfly. Just as some crawling, leaf-munching insects eventually become flying nectar-sipping insects, many other animals also go through changes in the course of their life cycles. Most changes, however, are far less radical. Kittens, ducklings, and fawns, for example, are structurally more similar to their parents than many newborn insects are, but young animals often have different markings that act to camouflage them.

Most young birds and mammals need parental care because they are not fully developed. Compare any downy, clumsy baby bird to its plumed and agile parents. Though the majority of young mammals closely resemble the adults of their species in appearance, they still must develop survival behaviour.

Alligators care for their young, but most amphibians, reptile, fish, and insects lay their eggs and depart. The young must fend for themselves immediately upon entering the world.

CURIOSITY PLACE

Hercules moths of Australia and New Guinea can have a wingspan of more than 30 cm.

Discuss whether the class is caring for the larva properly. Ask:

> **How do you know the larva has everything it needs?**
>
> **Are you being careful not to handle the larva?**
>
> **How can you tell whether the larva has the right food?**

Encourage the children to predict the next stage of the larva's life cycle. Ask:

> **Will the animal look the same at the next stage of its life cycle?**
>
> **Will the animal eat the same food?**
>
> **Will it live in the same place?**

Write down the children's responses and review them at the end of the unit.

Preconceptions

Children may believe the pupa and the adult insect are completely different animals. Emphasizing the constant traits of the animal throughout the life cycle may help to address this confusion.

ESL Learners

Spend some extra time with ESL children studying the photographs on page 12 of the Student Book. Point out the changes from egg to larva to pupa to adult animal. Help them develop the language to talk about the changes.

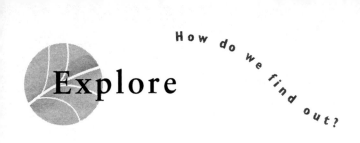

Explore

How do we find out?

Read page 12 from the Student Book with students. Talk about the changes the butterfly goes through. Now begin the Exploration.

Exploration

Observe a change.

1. It will usually take 7 to 10 days for the adult to emerge from the pupa. Ask the children to predict whether each adult will emerge at the same time. Ask them to tell why they think so. After about 5 days, have the children make butterfly food. They will need to mix 25 mL of sugar with 125 mL of water for every larva house. They should then soak the cotton balls in the sugar water and place the balls at the base of each larva house.

2. When the pupa opens, have the children draw a picture of the adult in their Science Journals. Ask them to observe carefully, then use colour and note as many details as possible. Have them discuss why all of the adults did or did not emerge at the same time (entered the pupa stage at different time; took varying times to develop, just as human babies do)

3. The children now have a last chance to watch the adult. Upon hatching, the adult will pump its wings for one to two hours to prepare for flight. The class may also see red liquid drop from the tail end of the butterfly. Tell them this is normal. Have children draw and write these and other observations in their Science Journals.

4. After a day, the children should release the adult. The whole class can observe the adult in flight.

THINK!
It is important to let the adult animal go because it can satisfy its needs better if it is free.

Exploration Results

Children should discover that although different, the larva, pupa, and adult are all part of the same life cycle. At each stage, the developing animal has changing needs; for example, the pupa feeds off food gel and the adult off sugar water. Looking after animals requires knowledge, respect, and careful treatment.

 Troubleshooting

The adult's wings are delicate. Don't allow the children to handle the newly hatched butterfly.

Apply

What did we learn?

Explain to children that the adult that emerges from the pupa is an insect. Insects hatch from eggs outside their mother's body. An insect has six legs, three main body parts (head, thorax, and abdomen), two antennae, and usually one or two pairs of wings. Distribute Reproducible 5A: *What Is an Insect?* Have the class label the insect parts.

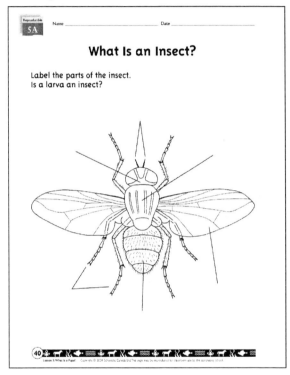

Refer the children to the drawings in their Science Journal. Ask them to check whether the adult butterfly has all the parts of an insect. As a class, describe this insect's life cycle using the words "larva," "pupa," and "adult." Then compare the appearance and activity of the larva with the adult insect. Ask:

Did the larva become a pupa and hatch again before it looked like its parent?

Together, try to calculate how long it took this insect to go from birth to adulthood.

Have the children predict what will come next in the adult insect's life (for example, laying eggs).

Extending Learning

Have the children think about why the butterfly should be released. Ask whether they have seen butterflies at home, how these butterflies behaved, and what they needed to survive. Then question the children about whether they could create a proper habitat for the butterfly. Explain that a butterfly's environment is very special and not easy to re-create.

Global Perspectives

Silk cloth is woven from the animal fibre that silkworms produce to make their cocoons. Hundreds of years ago, the Chinese invented the technique for harvesting and weaving silk. The Chinese silkworm produces more silk than any other caterpillar. Each one may spin a continuous thread of up to almost 750 m long.

Integrating Science

Art: Make a Model
Have the children recall the painted ladies or other butterflies they have seen. Using clothespins and paper towels, the children can make model butterflies. They can moisten the paper towels and then decorate them with markers or paint to resemble wings. Sliding a clothespin down the middle of the towel will provide the body. The clothespin body can be decorated with markers.

More Science: Plant a Garden
If there is a butterfly conservatory in your area, you might want to organize a field trip there. Through the field trip and/or class research, find out what kinds of plants will attract butterflies to your plot. Many of these will be native plants, such as beebalm or cornflower. Supervise the planting of the garden and wait for the butterflies to visit.

Name _____ Date _____

What Is an Insect?

Label the parts of the insect.
Is a larva an insect?

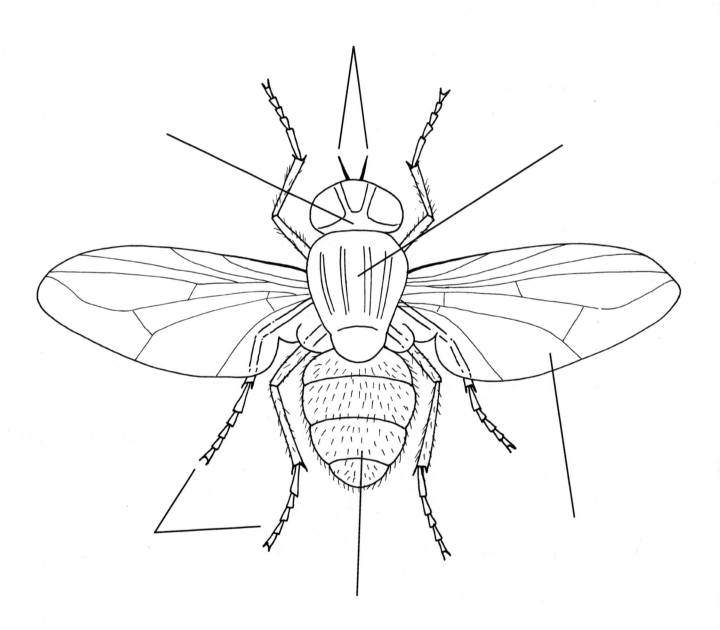

What Is a Pupa?

Draw or write what is missing.

1. egg ⟶ larva ⟶ [ ] ⟶ butterfly

2. butterfly ⟶ egg ⟶ [ ] ⟶ pupa

3. larva ⟶ pupa ⟶ butterfly ⟶ [ ]

4. pupa ⟶ [ ] ⟶ egg ⟶ larva

How Do Baby Robins Change?

Student Book pages 14–15

In this lesson: Children explore the life cycles of birds.

Outcomes

Children will have opportunities to:
• classify familiar animals according to similarities and differences in appearance, behaviour, and life cycles (T1)
• describe how animals are important in the lives of Aboriginal peoples in BC (T3)
• describe ways in which animals are important to other living things and the environment (T4)
• use the five senses to make observations (P1)
• communicate observations, experiences, and thinking in a variety of ways (P3)
• classify objects, events, and organisms (P4)
• use their senses to interpret observations (P5)

Assessment

• Assess children's presentation skills in the Activate. (P3)
• Ask each child to draw the life cycles of a robin and a butterfly. Through their drawings, children will demonstrate their understanding of the life cycle of a bird and some of the differences between birds. (T1, P4)
• Hand out Reproducible 6B: *What Animal...?* (Answers: 1. bird 2. fish 3. bird 4. fish) (T1, P4)
• Conduct a follow-up discussion on the issues raised in Apply. You will find out what children have learned about how animals care for their young. Ask:

How do baby robins change? How do they stay the same?
How do robin parents care for baby robins? Is this the same as how mammals care for their young?
Describe how some animals protect their young. (T1, T4, P4, P5)

• Have the children write or draw a short story about someone they feel has achieved something special and deserves to be awarded an eagle feather. (T3)

Getting Organized

Materials: Reproducible 6A: *How Do Animals Care for Their Young?* on page 46 and Reproducible 6B: *What Animal...?* on page 47; bird feathers, a bird's nest (both optional); modelling clay, and pictures for ESL learners

Suggested Grouping: class and individuals

Time Required: Activate 10–15 min; Explore 25–30 min plus 10– to 15–minute periods at home over several days; Apply 35–40 min

Advance Preparation: none

Safety: Examine feathers carefully for any evidence of "pests" before allowing children to handle them.

Lesson Vocabulary

bird: a warm-blooded, feathered animal with wings and a beak. It lays eggs from which its babies hatch.

Activate

Content Background

Most newly hatched birds look like fleshy blobs. First they grow down, then feathers. Both male and female baby birds are plain looking (to help camouflage them).

After the birds lose their baby feathers and grow their adult plumage, the males and females often develop different physical characteristics. Adult male birds are generally more brightly coloured than the adult female birds. Blue Jays are an exception to this pattern.

No bird can survive without its feathers. Primary feathers—those growing from a bird's wing tips—enable a bird to fly. In the moulting process—which occurs twice a year—a bird loses its primary feathers gradually. Likewise, the other contour feathers and down feathers, all vital to a healthy bird, are shed.

Preconceptions

Some children may think that animals can decide how many eggs to lay.

CURIOSITY PLACE

Many birds partly digest food before depositing it into their babies' beaks.

Explain to the children that a robin is a bird. Birds hatch from eggs. They have beaks, wings, and feathers.

Bring in some bird feathers and, if possible, a bird's nest. Circulate these among the children. Ask questions such as:

How does a bird build a nest?

Are bird feathers strong or fragile? hard or soft?

Do all birds have feathers? Why do you think they have feathers?

Do other kinds of animals have feathers? mammals? reptiles?

Do all birds fly?

Children may think that birds have feathers in order to fly. This is true, but it isn't the only reason. Some birds, of course, do not fly. Feathers provide warmth and protection from moisture. You might ask if the children are familiar with duvets and what some are stuffed with. Down is used because it is especially warm. It is also used in much of our winter clothing.

Ask children to contribute any questions they have about birds. Make a list and ask each child to pick a question. Once they have the answer to their question, they should present the answer to the rest of the class with an oral presentation, a poster, a model, and so on.

ESL Learners

Provide some modelling clay. Invite ESL children to make an accurate model of a newborn baby bird and an older baby bird. You could provide pictures for children to work from.

Read pages 14-15 of the Student Book with the class. Then encourage the children to describe the life cycle of a robin: features that change (eyes open, grow feathers, can fly) and features that remain through adulthood (have beak, wings, legs, eyes).

Then compare the robin with another bird. Ask:

Use what you know about the life cycle of a robin to think about a chicken's life cycle.

Lead the children to conclude that animals with similar life cycles to the robin are also birds. Then remind the children about the life cycle of an insect. Ask:

How are the life cycles of a bird and an insect the same? (both start out as an egg and grow and change until they are old enough to lay their own eggs)

How are they different? (birds need to care for their young; once they grow feathers, they look much the same for the rest of their lives; insects have distinctive stages—larva, pupa, and chrysalis; there is no resemblance between the baby and adult insect)

Exploration Results

Children should discover that all animals develop throughout the life cycle. Some traits stay the same and others change. Animals of the same class (for example, birds, reptiles, mammals) mostly have a similar life cycle. The life cycle of some animals, such as robins, may depend on migration.

Extending Learning

Provide as wide-ranging a list as you can of local animals and have the children choose two, then do a think/pair/share to describe and compare how each animal cares for its young. Provide time for them to do library research and allow class time for some of the children to present their findings.

Discuss page 15 in the Student Book. Explain that some birds eat worms and insects, and other birds eat seeds. Some birds even eat fish or small mammals. Now ask:

What would happen to these baby robins if their parent did not care for them?

Explain that baby robins cannot stand up, see, fly, or feed themselves. They would not survive alone. Discuss other ways that adult robins care for their babies (for example, protecting them from danger and harsh weather). Now ask:

What do you know about mammals?

How do mammals care for their young?

Then have the children describe what they know about other animals (for example, dogs, cats, horses) and how they care for their young. Then ask:

What do you know about insects?

Do insects care for their young?

Explain to the children that insects do not care for their young.

Have students do Reproducible 6A: *How Do Animals Care for Their Young?* The answers are: muskoxen (We form a circle around our young with our heads and horns facing the danger.), **bear** (I will fight to protect my cubs!), **sea turtle** (I lay my eggs and then use my large flippers to hide my nest with sand.), **kill deer** (I pretend to have a hurt wing to keep a predator away from my nest.), **gafftopsail catfish** (I carry them in my mouth while I swim.).

Ask them how they know what belongs together.

Integrating Science

Interview an Expert

Invite a local biologist or wildlife specialist to show slides, or if possible, to bring in live birds. Ask the expert to talk about where the various birds live and how they survive. Before the visit, ask students to think of at least one question to ask the expert.

Language Arts: Write a Story

Remind children of how adult animals often protect their babies from danger. Have each child write a story describing the dramatic rescue of some baby animals by their parents.

Social Studies: Give a Presentation

Divide the children into small groups. Ask each group to brainstorm how humans use birds (for example, eggs and meat for food, feathers for warmth or decoration). If you have any First Nations children in your class, they should be able to describe how First Nations people present eagle feathers to those who have achieved something. The feathers represent honour and freedom (see resources on page 11). The children should take notes. Then have each group present their findings to the class.

Global Perspectives

About 100 years ago, large wading birds in the southern United States nearly became extinct. The herons, egrets, spoonbills, and other birds were killed for their beautiful feathers. Humans wanted the feathers to decorate their clothes and hats. Only about 10 percent of these beautiful birds have survived.

CURIOSITY PLACE

After hatching, some baby birds follow the first moving thing they see. This is how chicks learn to stay with their mother. If confused, chicks may follow a human or even a football.

THINK!

At first, young robins need to be fed and protected. Later they must learn survival skills from their parents.

Name _____ Date _____

How Do Animals Care for Their Young?

Draw lines to match the right pictures and descriptions.
To protect my young:

I lay my eggs and then use my large flippers to hide my nest with sand.

I carry them in my mouth while I swim.

I will fight to protect my cubs!

We form a circle around our young with our heads and horns facing the danger.

I pretend to have a hurt wing to keep predators away from my nest.

What Animal...?

Circle the right answer.

1. This animal lays a few eggs.

2. This animal lays many, many eggs.

3. This animal takes care of its babies.

4. This animal does not take care of its babies.

What Happens to Animals in Winter?

Student Book pages 16–17

In this lesson: Children explore ways animals cope with winter. Children also construct a bird feeder.

Outcomes

Children will have opportunities to:
- classify familiar animals according to similarities and differences in appearance, behaviour, and life cycles (T1)
- describe some changes that affect animals (T2)
- describe ways in which animals are important to other living things and the environment (T4)
- use the five senses to make observations (P1)
- communicate their observations, experiences, and thinking in a variety of ways (P3)
- classify objects, events, and organisms (P4)
- infer the probable outcome of an event or behaviour based on observations (P5)

Assessment

- Review the children's Science Journals. Review the group work they did on migration. The children's drawings and notes should demonstrate their understanding of migration and the kinds of habitats and food suitable for birds. (T1, T2, T4, P3)
- Take note of students' contributions to the conversations. (T1)
- Collect the Science Journals and review how children documented the Exploration. Children should have observed how birds use the hand-made feeder and how they, as humans, were able to help an animal. (T3, T4, P1, P3, P4, P6)
- Reproducibles 7A and 7B will help you assess children's understanding of migration and hibernation. (T1, T2, T4, P4)

Getting Organized

Materials: Reproducible 7A: *Follow the Butterflies* on page 52 and Reproducible 7B: *Where Will We Spend the Winter?* on page 53; 1-L cardboard milk containers or plastic pop bottles, scissors, pencils or twigs, string, sunflower seeds or other bird seed

Suggested Grouping: class and groups of three or four

Time Required: Activate 10–15 min; Explore 25–30 min; Apply 15-20 min

Advance Preparation: Send home a letter to parents requesting milk cartons or plastic pop bottles.

Safety: Oversee use of scissors. Instruct children to get help from an adult in hanging their feeder at home.

Lesson Vocabulary

hibernate: Some animals hibernate or sleep during the winter months. At this time, their heart and breathing rates are lowered.

migrate: When animals migrate, they travel from one place to another because of the change of season and weather. Sometimes they travel very long distances.

Activate

What do we know? What do we want to know? What do we know?

Content Background

When winter arrives, warmth and food become hard to find. Plants die or become dormant until spring, relying on food stored in their roots to survive the winter. Animals often eat food that they gathered and buried during summer and fall.

The metabolisms of animals that hibernate slow down; heart rates and body temperatures fall. Amphibians bury themselves in mud, while rodents burrow into dens. Bears nap for the whole season, awakening only occasionally.

Many animals migrate, returning home in the spring. Birds travel along flyways to the same destinations each year.

Mammals are warm-blooded. They must remain active if they don't migrate or hibernate. Many mammals grow thicker fir in winter, which helps ward off the cold.

Many migrating birds travel from the Northern to the Southern Hemisphere for the winter. Birds in tropical climates may also migrate in response to wet and dry seasons. Most birds migrate in flocks.

Explore what the children know about migration and introduce the definition. Keep in mind that animal migration and hibernation will vary across Canada depending on climate. Ask:

In cold weather, do we see robins?

Where do you think robins go in cold weather?

What do other animals do in winter?

If some children have lived in other countries, ask them to share what they know about animal migration there.

Troubleshooting

Children in British Columbia and Southern Ontario may argue that robins do not migrate. These children may see robins in the winter. Explain that some robins do migrate from some parts of Canada.

Preconceptions

Children may puzzle over why an animal would expend so much energy on migration. One purpose of this lesson is to explain how some animals must migrate to survive.

Explore

Divide the children into groups of three or four. Have each group research a different animal that migrates. Have them discuss in their groups, then draw or note in their Science Journals the kinds of habitats through which the animals will travel and the kinds of food they might find. Allow time for the groups to share their findings with the class.

Explain that some birds (but not robins) eat seeds. Feeding birds can help them through the winter, when food is hard to find. Now get ready to make individual feeders and one class feeder.

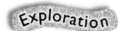

Make a birdfeeder.

1. Prepare the materials. First, make sure the milk containers or plastic pop bottles are clean. Have the children cut a window in each container that is big enough for a bird to enter. Then have the children cut two holes in the middle of the container and add a twig or pencil to create a perch. Finally, have the children cut two more holes at the top of the container and thread the yarn through them to hang the feeder.
2. Fill the feeders with seeds. (See Troubleshooting.) You might ask if any of the children already have feeders at home. Encourage any who do to tell the class what they know about the types of seeds that are used in their feeder. They might be able to describe how different types of seeds can be used to attract specific species of birds.
3. Hang one feeder outside the classroom. Explain that feeders can be hung from stable tree branches or posts but should be kept away from squirrels. Ask the children to take home their feeders and hang them.

Remind the children that they will need to refill the feeders when they are empty.
4. Have the children regularly observe the birds at the school and home feeders. Encourage them to write and draw their observations in their Science Journal. The children should be noting what kinds of birds visit the feeder, how they eat, and when and how much they eat. Ask the children whether any baby birds visit the feeders. If not, ask why.

Exploration Results

Children should become aware that different birds have different diets. In winter, food can be scarce and people can help seed-eating birds by providing feed. Very young birds will not visit the feeder.

Troubleshooting

Explain to the children that not all birds feed on the same seed. Sunflower seeds attract a variety of birds.

CURIOSITY PLACE

The Arctic tern has a migratory route that extends 15 000 km from the Arctic Circle to the Antarctic.

Apply

What did we learn?

Hand out Reproducible 7A: *Follow the Butterflies*. Explain that monarch butterflies migrate to warm places in the winter. There, thousands of monarchs live in trees and then fly back north in the spring. Female monarchs lay their eggs on the way back and then die.

Have the children mark the migration route of the monarchs on the map. An excellent website is www.monarchwatch.org/

Ask children if they need to eat while they sleep. Do animals? Explain that some animals—frogs, turtles, bears, some snakes, and raccoons—sleep, or hibernate, in winter. They may go under the mud, into caves, underground, or into people's attics. Describe how hibernating animals eat a lot in the late fall to store enough fat for the winter.

Now, ask:

How can animals that do not hibernate survive? (migrate, store food for winter, grow thicker fur, develop an extra layer of fat)

How does a grizzly (or black) bear survive? (hibernates)

an Arctic hare? (grows thicker fur)

a blue jay? (uses feeders)

Point out that some mammals grow longer fur; some animals change colour for camouflage; some birds visit feeders.

Encourage the children to use the Internet and CD-ROMs to research the winter habitats of northern animals.

Now hand out Reproducible 7B: *Where Will We Spend the Winter?* (snake in burrow, raccoon in attic, turtle in pond, bear in cave)

Extending Learning

Remind the children that monarch butterflies live in trees during the winter. Ask them what would happen if humans cut down these important trees. Discuss how humans can affect other animals.

As a class, brainstorm what animals need to survive in any environment (food and shelter). Discuss how you and the children have helped birds by making and filling the bird feeders. Ask how else people might help birds (provide bird houses where they can nest; and provide fresh water, especially during very cold weather when their usual water sources might be frozen).

Encourage the children to consider the flip side of this situation: what kinds of things do people do that make survival difficult for animals? (being inconsistent about providing food and water for birds; damaging animals' environment, including our own, in some way). You can deal with this subject fairly superficially, which might be most appropriate for this age group. If you wish and if you feel your students can handle these ideas, you might want to ask how the children feel about destroying some animal. A good example, would be the mosquito. Children probably wouldn't regret seeing the end of that species. Nevertheless, it's important for the children to understand that the mosquito is an important part of the food chain that other animals depend on it, and if we eradicate it, some animals will lose a crucial food source.

You might suggest that children establish a "How We Affect Animals" Centre, and add their ideas as they continue through the unit.

THINK!
The animals that stay over winter will vary from region to region.

Name _____ Date _____

Follow the Butterflies

On the map, mark the migration route
of the monarch butterflies.

Will all the butterflies return north in
the spring?

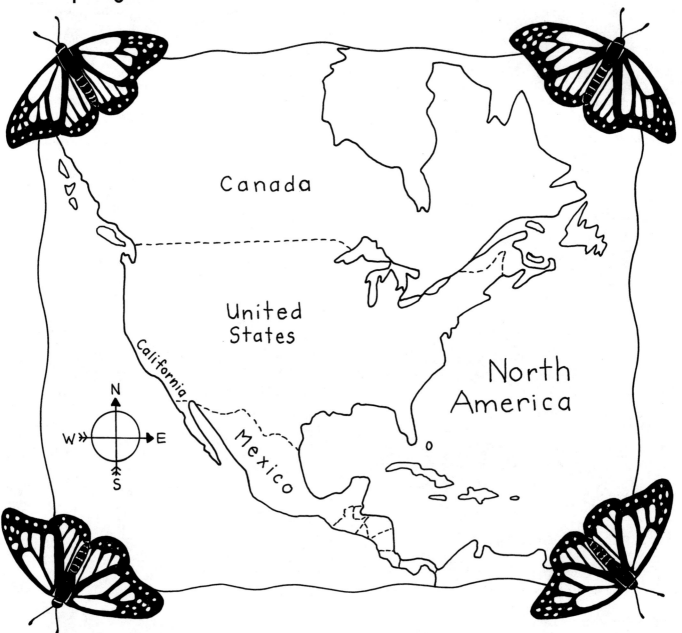

Lesson 7: What Happens to Animals in Winter?   Copyright © 2004 Scholastic Canada Ltd. This page may be reproduced for classroom use by the purchasing school.

Where Will We Spend the Winter?

Cut out the four animals that hibernate in the places shown.
Now paste each animal into the right place.

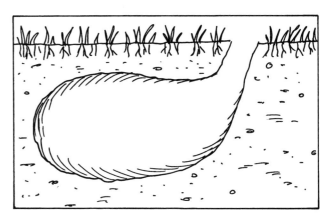

Where Do Animals Live?

Student Book pages 18–19

In this lesson: Children discover where animals live.

Outcomes

Children will have opportunities to:
- classify familiar animals according to similarities and differences in appearance, behaviour, and life cycles (T1)
- describe some changes that affect animals (T2)
- describe ways in which animals are important to other living things and the environment (T4)
- use the five senses to make observations (P1)
- share with others information obtained by observing (P2)
- classify objects, events, and organisms (P4)
- use their senses to interpret observations (P5)
- infer the probable outcome of an event or behaviour based on observations (P6)

Assessment

- Note the children's responses to the questions in Explore and Apply. (T1, T2, T4, P1, P2, P4, P5, P6)
- Assess the children's answers on Reproducible 8A. (T1, P4, P6)
- Have the children complete Reproducible 8B: *What Is My Life Cycle?* on page 59. (Answers: Newt-egg, larva, newt. Frog-egg, tadpole, frog. The frog eggs and the tadpole should be in the water. Newts and frogs can be either in the water or on land.) (T1, P6)

Getting Organized

Materials: Reproducible 8A: *Who Lives Here?* on page 58 and Reproducible 8B: *What Is My Life Cycle?* on page 59; caged animal or fish in bowl (optional)

Suggested Grouping: class, pairs, and individual

Time Required: Activate 10–15 min; Explore 40 min plus field trip; Apply 30 min

Advance Preparation: Arrange to bring in a small pet in a cage or a fish in a bowl. Take note of places wild animals in the school area can often be seen. Plan a trip to a zoo, an aquarium, or a farm.

Safety: Find out about children's allergies before selecting a pet to bring in. Do not let children put their fingers into an animal's cage. Supervise children closely on field trips.

Lesson Vocabulary

amphibian: a cold-blooded animal that can live both in and out of the water. Amphibians breathe with gills when they are young and with lungs as adults. Frogs and salamanders are examples of amphibians.

Content Background

Animal habitats are very diverse: from grasslands to oceans, deserts to tropical rain forests, and mountains to grasslands.

Every animal has a home range, where it is born, lives, and dies. The size of an animal's range varies. It reflects the availability of food and water and places to breed.

Some environments host many animals. In a city alley, raccoons, squirrels, tomcats, rats, mice, cockroaches, and other animals may share space.

In the harshest environments, animals must be resourceful to survive (for example, in Northern Canada). To conserve warmth, most northern species have developed short extremities. For instance, the Arctic fox has short ears, muzzle, legs, and tail. Many smaller mammals, such as mice and shrews, retreat beneath the snow for insulation. Aquatic mammals, such as beavers and otters, build lodges or burrows in banks to warm themselves when out of the water.

The spread of humans is endangering many animal habitats. Humans are now trying to correct the damage by protecting disappearing habitats. For instance, Kruger Park in South Africa includes tropical forest, desert, savanna, and bamboo regions. This park protects wildebeest, rhinoceros, and gorillas among others. Banff National Park was the first national park in the world and Wood Buffalo National Park is one of the biggest in the world.

Bring in a small animal in a cage (bird, guinea pig, mouse) or a fish in an aquarium. The animal could be a class pet or one of the children's pets. Have the children examine the animal in its human-made environment. Ask:

What things does this animal need to survive?
(food, shelter, air)

How does it get them?

Then suggest to the children that some animals live in more than one environment. For instance, a seal spends time on the land and in the water. Ask:

Can you think of any other animals that live in more than one place?
(frogs, alligators, monarch butterflies, Canada geese)

Do you think any animals might live in one place when they are young and another place when they are older? Which ones?
(frogs, salmon)

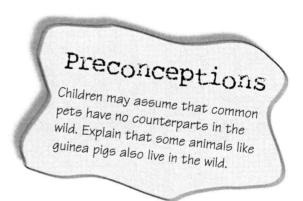

Preconceptions

Children may assume that common pets have no counterparts in the wild. Explain that some animals like guinea pigs also live in the wild.

Explore

How do we find out?

Have the children read page 18 of the Student Book. Then ask them to answer Think! on page 19.

Once the children have defined the life cycle of a frog, discuss the word "amphibian." Explain that a frog is an amphibian. Ask them if they can think of other animals that are amphibian (toads, salamanders). Then ask the class to recall the life cycle of a mammal. Ask:

Is a cow's life cycle the same as or different from a frog's? (both begin life as eggs, change and grow as they get older, have babies and die; a frog changes from having to live in water to breathing to being able to live on land.)

Do you think a cow is an amphibian? Why or why not? (can't live in water, has fur)

Tell the class about the life cycle of an amphibian other than a frog; for example, a newt (egg, gill-breathing larval stage, lung-breathing terrestrial stage). By comparing a newt's life cycle with a frog's, the children should conclude that a newt is also an amphibian.

Discuss where frogs live and why. Then refer the children to the first sentence on page 18 of the Student Book, "Animals live where they can breathe, find food, and have babies." Remind children that to breathe, eat, and reproduce, a frog needs to live in different environments at different stages of its life cycle.

Troubleshooting

Before asking the class to find animals near the school, make sure that you are aware of two or three places nearby where wild animals live in their natural habitat. Consider, too, the time of day when these animals are active, and schedule the nature walk at a time when the animals are likely to appear.

Exploration

Take a nature walk.

1. Before you take the children outside, discuss places where they might see animals. Ask them to suggest what they can do to see more animals (keep quiet and stay still). Encourage the children to work in pairs. Even in urban areas, both squirrels and birds should be accessible. In their Science Journals, have the children document how the animals live and what they eat. Remind the children not to touch the animals.
2. The children should now record (i.e., draw or write) how they expect these animals to change throughout the life cycle.
3. Finally, ask whether these animals are living in a good place and why. Again, have the children respond (draw or write) in their Science Journals.

CURIOSITY PLACE

A black bear may have a home that extends over hundreds of hectares. That is much bigger than Toronto or Vancouver.

Exploration Results

Children should discover that wild animals live in almost every environment. In pictures and/or words, children should note some things that help animals to survive. Children should consider whether the animals' habitats suit them ideally and whether these habitats can fill the animals' needs at all stages of the life cycle.

Apply

What did we learn?

Review the observations from the nature walk. Explain to the children that the animals they studied were in their natural environment. As a contrast, remind the class that the fish in the aquarium or the animal in the cage from the beginning of the lesson (Activate) was in a human-made environment. Have the children recall the features of the natural environment that promote the survival (i.e., health and growth) of the animals they saw outside.

Arrange for the children to visit a human-made environment for animals. They could visit a public aquarium, a zoo, or a farm. Encourage them to ask questions about what they are learning. If this proves impossible, use resources within your school, such as an aquarium. Have the children respond in their Science Journals to the same questions they answered on the nature walk (for example, where the animals live and what they eat, how they change throughout the life cycle, whether their environment is a good one). Also ask:

How have humans made this a place where animals can live?

Do you think this human-made place is as good for the animals as the natural places where they would live? Why or why not?

Have the children draw or write their conclusions in their Science Journals.

Extending Learning

Discuss with the class what might happen if an animal cannot find the right place to live. Do they think the animal will die? Will it live elsewhere? Do humans ever affect where an animal lives? Give children Reproducible 8A: *Who Lives Here?*

Remind the children to add their ideas to the "How We Affect Animals" Centre.

Integrating Science

Art: Make a Model
Divide the children into pairs. Ask each group to select an amphibian and model it in clay. One child should model the larval phase and the other the adult phase of the life cycle.

Physical Education: Exercise Your Imagination
Lead the class in a series of exercises inspired by the life cycle of an amphibian. On mats, imitate the swimming of tadpoles and the slithering of salamanders. Then bounce up and down like frogs.

THINK!
A frog begins its life cycle as an egg. The egg becomes a tadpole that lives in the water. Then the tadpole grows into a baby frog that leaves the water. Although frogs need to breathe air, most like to live near water.

Name _____   Date _____

Who Lives Here?

This is a house and garden where humans live.
What kind of animals might live around the house?
Draw them in.

Reproducible
8B

What Is My Life Cycle?

The newt and the frog are both amphibians.
List the stages in the life cycle of an amphibian.
Now circle the eggs or animals that are in the wrong place.

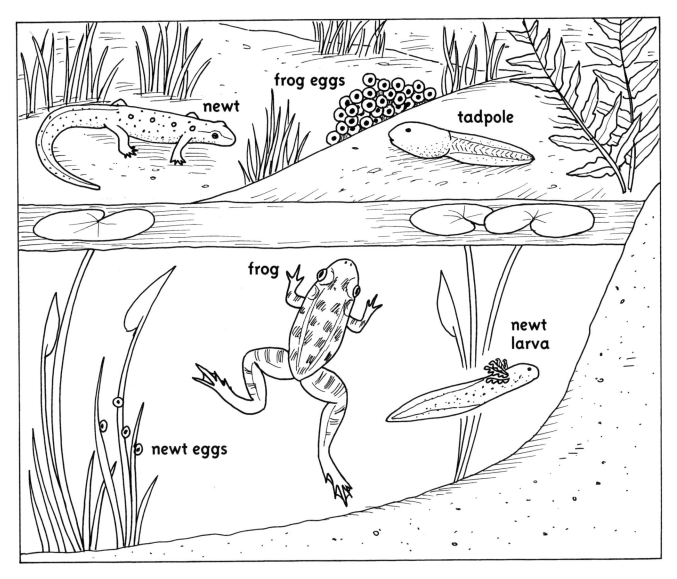

Newt

1. _____

2. _____

3. _____

Frog

1. _____

2. _____

3. _____

What Is a Human's Life Cycle?

Student Book pages 20–21

In this lesson: Children learn about the human life cycle.

Outcomes

Children will have opportunities to:
- classify familiar animals according to similarities and differences in appearance, behaviour, and life cycles (T1)
- describe ways in which animals are important to other living things and the environment (T4)
- use the five senses to make observations (P1)
- share with others information obtained by observing (P2)
- classify objects, events, and organisms (P4)
- infer the probable outcome of an event or behaviour based on observations (P6)

Assessment

- Take note of students' answers to your questions in the Explore and Apply sections to assess what children understand about how animals survive and care for their young. (T1, T4, P1, P2, P4, P6)
- Hand out Reproducible 9B: *Animals Grow Up* on page 65. The responses will help you assess whether children can compare human growth with that of another animal. (T1, P4)
- Ask students to compare (in writing, pictures, or orally) what a human baby needs to survive with what another baby animal needs. (T1, P1, P2, P6)

Getting Organized

Materials: Reproducible 9A: *Why Do Some Animals Grow Up Quickly?* on page 64 and Reproducible 9B: *Animals Grow Up* on page 65; a real baby and/or pictures of babies

Suggested Grouping: class and individual

Time Required: Activate 10–15 min; Explore 15–20 min; Apply 20 min

Advance Preparation: You may wish to try to arrange for a real baby to visit the class. Do not allow the children to pick up the baby, and take care that they do not overwhelm or otherwise upset it.

Content Background

Humans belong to the group of placental, or higher, mammals. The human life cycle begins in the female ovary with the ripening of an egg, which then travels into the fallopian tube, or oviduct.

After fertilization by a male sperm, the egg, which is minute, begins to grow very quickly. Within 30 hours of fertilization, the egg becomes two cells. After three days, the developing egg has become 32 cells.

About a week after fertilization, the growing egg attaches itself to the wall of the womb. That is when the placenta, or protective covering, forms around the egg or embryo. By connecting the mother's bloodstream with the embryo, the placenta brings nourishment to the fetus and eliminates its waste. The placenta is unique to higher mammals.

The nine-month gestation period of a human is long compared with that of many animals, even other mammals. Some fish and reptile eggs need only a few weeks to develop. Cats have about a three-month gestation period. Elephants have a gestation period of about 22 months.

Once a human baby is born, it needs a longer period of parental care than any other animal.

Activate

What do we know? *What do we want to know?*

Try to have a baby visit the classroom at this time. Perhaps one of the children has an infant sibling that the parent would be willing to bring in. If a real baby visit cannot be arranged, you may wish to bring in some photos of babies sleeping, eating, and so on. Encourage students to ask questions about babies and their care.

Now invite the children to observe the baby and/or to share experiences they have had with babies at home. Ask:

What is a baby like when it is just born?

Can a baby see or hear?

How does it eat?

Does it sleep a lot?

In their Science Journals, have the children draw or write the observations prompted by these questions. Then ask:

What skills might an older baby have?

When does a child stop being a baby? Why do you think so?

Encourage children to talk to their families about how babies develop.

ESL Learners

Question the children about how infants feed, sleep, move, and so on. Have the children point to pictures that show the correct response or have them draw a response in their Science Journals.

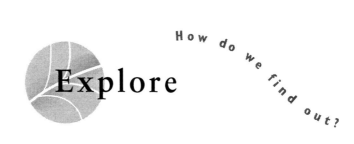

Explore

How do we find out?

Read page 20 in the Student Book and then point out the graph on page 21. Encourage the children to study the graph, and make sure they understand how to read it. Ask:

What animals are listed on the graph?

There are humans on this graph. Are humans also animals?

How do we know that humans are animals?

Explain that humans, like other animals, have a life cycle. For the children to complete the rest of the lesson, it is essential that they understand that humans are part of the animal world.

Preconceptions

Understandably, children may confuse "baby" with "young child." They may be used to calling a younger sibling of four or five "my baby sister" or "my baby brother." A true baby depends entirely on its parents for survival. Children at different stages of growth may be called toddlers, preschoolers, school-age children, or adolescents.

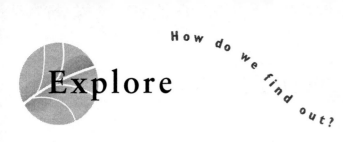

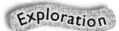

Study the graph.

Ask the children questions such as:

Why do you think some animals grow up faster than other animals?
(their life span is shorter, they develop the skills they need to survive faster—their development is less complex)

Are some baby animals in more danger than others? Why?
(they don't have parents to protect them)

Do some need to move and find food right away? Why?
(they don't have anyone to feed them)

Once the children have suggested some ideas, circulate Reproducible 9A: *Why Do Some Animals Grow Up Quickly?*. (Answers: 1. true 2. false 3. true 4. false)

Exploration Results

Children should discover that humans and other animals grow at different rates. How fast an animal grows is related to many factors: the length of its life cycle, the complexity of the animal, and the behaviours needed for survival. Good health cannot significantly accelerate the life cycle.

Troubleshooting

Make sure the children understand that good parental care and fast growth are not necessarily related. A human baby, for instance, needs many years to mature, even with excellent care from its parents, because it is a complex organism.

Now return to the graph on page 21 of the Student Book. Discuss the graph with the children, and ask them to describe how long each animal takes to become an adult. Ask:

Is there a big or small difference in how long each animal takes to become an adult?

Which animal on the graph grows fastest?

Which animal on the graph grows slowest?

Explain that baby animals cannot protect or feed themselves very well. Remind children that mammals must nurse directly from their parents. Have the children consult the chart once again. Ask:

Which of the animals on the chart are mammals?

Do humans, who are looked after by their parents, need more time to grow than other animals?

Then ask:

What other animals besides mammals are shown on the graph?

Do these animals grow faster than mammals?

Do they live longer or shorter lives than mammals?

CURIOSITY PLACE

In well-off countries like Canada, many humans now live to be 80 years old. A hundred years ago, few humans lived to be more than 40 years old.

Extending Learning

Have the children recall what they learned about baby robins in Lesson 6. Then ask them to figure out whether robins or humans take longer to become adults. Afterwards, ask the children to compare the life cycles of caterpillars and humans. Finally, ask them how long their pets remained babies compared with humans. Humans live longer than most animals. Do bigger animals live longer than small ones?

THINK!
Humans take longer than robins to become adults.

Integrating Science

Language Arts: Write a Story
Read children the poem "Fish Story" by Richard Armour (from *A Literature of Sports*, D.C. Heath & Co., 1980). Ask children to pretend that they are trout being raised on a fish farm. Have them write (and if they wish, draw) a story that describes their lives.

Mathematics: Use Manipulatives
Divide the children into groups, with each child representing one of the animals on the graph in the Student Book. Have each child count out manipulatives (for example, Unifix cubes) and join them together to represent the number of years it takes their animal to become an adult. (Since children might find mixed fractions confusing, round to the nearest year.) Have the children in each group compare their manipulatives to determine how much longer humans take to reach adulthood than other animals.

Alternatively, you might want to have the children use masking tape to measure out the timelines on the floor. Point out that the range they are measuring is very broad (1-1/2 weeks to 18 years). Encourage discussion about how they plan to measure: will they measure in years? months? If they mention that the bass takes less than a month to reach maturity, ask how they might turn that amount of time into months. If they don't suggest rounding, you might do that. They must then decide how they will represent the period of time (weeks, months, years) they have chosen. The children will need to make sure that they don't choose a unit of measure so small that they have no space in the room to indicate the largest number and that they don't choose one so large that the smallest number becomes virtually invisible. Invite them to convert each of the figures in the chart on page 21 into whichever unit they have selected and figure out how many units they will need. If they find their chosen unit isn't going to work very well, they may wish to choose another one.

Name _____ Date _____

Why Do Some Animals Grow Up Quickly?

Write true or false beside each sentence.

1. Some animals have a short life cycle.

_____

2. They might be eaten by another animal.

_____

3. They need to be strong enough to migrate.

_____

4. They hibernate.

_____

Animals Grow Up

Play "growing up" with two or three other children.

1. Make several copies of the cards. Cut out the cards and mix them together.
2. Put the cards face down in a pile.
3. Each player takes three cards.
4. Take turns drawing one card at a time.
5. If you pick a card you already have, put it back.
6. Try for two complete sets. Put the cards in order. Show the woman and the alligator growing up!

How Do Humans Change?

Student Book pages 22–23

In this lesson: Children investigate how humans change throughout the life cycle.

Outcomes

Children will have opportunities to:
• describe some changes that affect animals (T2)
• use their senses to interpret observations (P5)
• infer the probable outcome of an event or behaviour based on observations (P6)
Also T1, P1, P2, P3, P4

Assessment

• Collect children's charts. (T1, P1, P2, P3, P8)
• Have the children do Reproducible 10B: *Growing and Changing* on page 70. (Answers: 1. child and baby 2. bone, muscle 3. fingernail) (T1, T2, P1, P5, P6)

Getting Organized

Materials: Reproducible 10A: *Measure and Compare!* on page 69 and Reproducible 10B: *Growing and Changing* on page 70; a baby or young adult visitor; one or more adult volunteers; measuring tapes; photos of children's parents

Suggested Grouping: class and pairs/individual

Time Required: Activate 10–15 min; Explore 20 min; Apply 25–30 min

Advance Preparation: Arrange for a baby and/or young adult to visit with one or more adult volunteers. Ask children to bring in photos of their parents as babies and as adults.

Lesson Vocabulary

organ: a body part that has a special role in the bigger system of an animal

puberty: the phase of the life cycle when an animal becomes able to reproduce

Content Background

The first two years of human life are a time of extreme physical and intellectual growth. By 12 months, a baby begins to understand language, experience emotions, and have some muscle control. By two years, a child has usually reached half of its adult height and its brain growth is almost complete.

Motor skills and the ability to learn develop until the age of five. By this age, bones begin to lengthen and adult teeth may start to appear. Five-year-olds may have a vocabulary of 1500–2000 words.

Rapid growth slows down from the age of six until puberty. The onset of puberty in girls is usually between 10 and 14 years; in boys, it is slightly later. During puberty, the pituitary gland and sex glands become active. The hormones released enable the sexual development necessary for reproduction.

The human body is strongest in the twenties. After that, gradual aging begins. In old age, the body generally becomes stiffer and less lean. The nervous system and the skin are weaker. Important organs may work less well.

Activate

What do we know? *What do we want to know?*

Discuss the illustrations in the Student Book, pages 22–23, that document human growth and change. Have the children examine the models or photos. Then ask:

How do the humans we see change as they get older?

Are there ways that humans stay the same?

Which of these humans have grown enough to have babies of their own?

Record the answers on the board so the children can consult them later.

Preconceptions

Understandably, children may correlate size with age and stage of development. This lesson should clarify that individuals develop at different rates. For instance, a girl of 14 may be taller than many adult women and look fully developed. Unlike an adult woman, however, the girl is still growing.

Explore

How do we find out?

Explain to the children that they are going to measure some parts of their bodies. Read the instructions aloud from page 23 of the Student Book and make sure the children understand what they should do.

Exploration

Observe changes.

1. Pass around the measuring tapes (at least one for every two children). You may choose to have the children work in pairs, so that they can help measure each other.
2. If you have only one adult volunteer, have the children take turns measuring the adult's hand, foot, and arm and record the results in their Science Journals.
3. Again, have the children take turns measuring the baby or young adult and record the results in their journals.
4. Demonstrate how to make a chart with the information students have collected. Ask the children what changes they noted among the measurements for babies, themselves, the young adults, and the adults. You can ask the children to note similarities in the results, as well as differences, if appropriate.

Global Perspectives

Most healthy adult humans experience a phase in their life cycle when they are able to reproduce. Some people choose to have many children and some people choose not to have any at all. Being able to choose whether to reproduce makes humans different from other animals.

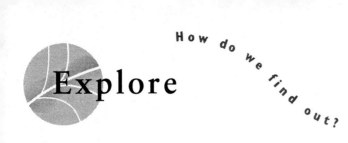

Explore

Apply

Troubleshooting

If the children are going to work in pairs, advise them to be gentle and touch only those body parts relevant to the activity. You may choose to have pairs of the same gender.

Exploration Results

Children should discover that hands, feet, and arms continue to grow until a human reaches adulthood. Growth is rapid in early life and then tends to slow. Although the length and proportions of the parts measured change, the number of fingers and toes is constant.

THINK!

The number of eyes, legs, and arms are some of the things that stay the same throughout the human life cycle. The colour and amount of hair, the number of teeth, and the body weight are among those things that change.

If the children have worked in pairs, have them remain with their partner. If the children have been working individually, divide them into pairs.

Have each pair examine the Step 1 results in the Science Journal for each partner. Explain that not all humans grow and develop at the same rate. This will become apparent as the children compare their Stage 1 results.

Now hand out Reproducible 10A: *Measure and Compare!* Working in pairs, and continuing to consult their Science Journals, the children should complete the activity.

When all the pairs have completed their measurements, model developing a graph for one of the body parts (the foot will probably give you the greatest variation in size). Ask each pair for the measurement they took of each other's foot. Write each new measurement horizontally on the chalkboard. When you get measurements that are the same, put a check mark under the appropriate measurement. To develop the graph, have the children count for you how many are in each size category. Discuss with the class how your graph might be divided along its left margin (e.g., by twos or fours). Draw the axes, and then encourage various children to come up and help you show where the bar should go (you can make this a bar graph, which is easy for the children to read, by using a measure that will avoid fractions (e.g., xx cm - xx cm, and so on).

Extending Learning

Have the children bring in baby photos and adult photos of their parents. Based on the photos, have a class discussion about which things change and which stay the same. Ask:

What kinds of changes do not come from growth?
(Changes that do not come from growth involve reproduction [females], learning, aging, and illness.)

Name _____ Date _____

Measure and Compare!

Draw your own hand, foot, and arm.
Mark in the correct measurements.
Now do the same for your partner.
Whose are bigger? Who is older?

hand	foot	arm

_____ _____ _____

hand	foot	arm

_____ _____ _____

Name _____   Date _____

Growing and Changing

Circle the right answers. There may be more than one right answer for each question.

1. Which of these humans is still growing?

  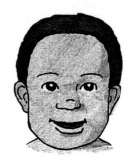

2. Which of these body parts gets weaker as a person gets older?

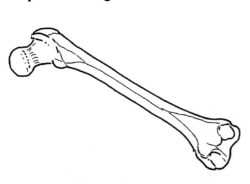  

3. Which of these body parts can grow?

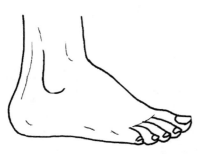  

You are still growing. Are other members of your family, too?

How Do Humans Grow?

Student Book pages 24–25

In this lesson: Children discover how humans need food to grow and remain healthy.

Outcomes

Children will have opportunities to:
- describe ways in which animals are important to other living things and the environment (T4)
- use their senses to interpret observations (P5)

Also T1, P1, P4

Assessment

- Review the children's charts on Reproducible 11B: *What Do I Eat?* on page 76. Did the children choose food from the four different groups? (As long as their diet allows them to eat foods from all four groups.) (T1, T4, P4)
- Remind children that they have learned a lot about the four food groups. Ask:

  What are the four groups? Give examples from each. Where does the food in each group come from? What happens to us if we do not get enough food from each group? (T1, T4, P4, P5)

Getting Organized

Materials: Reproducible 11A: *Where Does Food Come From?* on page 75 and Reproducible 11B: *What Do I Eat?* on page 76; pita bread, green pepper, tomato slices, cheese slices, pepperoni, tofu cubes; bowls, plates, and napkins (not disposable); a knife

Suggested Grouping: class and individuals

Time Required: Activate 10 min; Explore 15–20 min; Apply 20–25 min (students fill out chart of what they eat over a day)

Advance Preparation: Purchase pizza ingredients and cut them up.

Safety: Be aware of children's food allergies and dietary restrictions. Explain that some children cannot eat food from all four groups.

Content Background

All animals need food to survive. Food gives animals the energy to keep all parts of their body working. Different animals require different foods to stay healthy. Humans need a variety of foods.

The food group of grain products includes wheat, rice, and oats (whole grains include fibre and important vitamins). Foods from this group are rich in carbohydrates, needed to give us energy, but low in fat. For this reason, some nutritionists suggest that this food group form the largest single part of a person's diet.

Milk products include cheese, yogurt, and ice cream. Most of our milk comes from cows and sometimes goats. In other parts of the world, milk may come from sheep, camels, or llamas. Milk products contain calcium, carbohydrates, proteins, fats, and vitamins.

Vegetables and fruits are rich in vitamins and fibre. Fruits are the seed-bearing parts of a plant. Some fruits (eggplants and tomatoes) are commonly taken for vegetables. Vegetables are usually the roots, leaves, or stalks of a plant. Children may not be enthusiastic about this food group. In fact, many adults do not eat nearly enough fruits and vegetables for an optimum level of health.

Meat and alternatives supply much of the protein that a person needs. Meat is actually the muscle of an animal. The alternatives are largely legumes, or seeds that grow in pods, and tofu and other soy products that are lower in fat than meat and have no cholesterol.

Activate

What do we know? What What do we want to know?

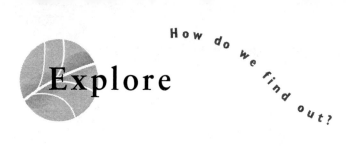
Have a few children recall what they had for dinner last night. List the ingredients for each meal on the board. Now ask the class:

Why do you need to eat?

Which of these meals is best for you? Why?

You may need to use sensitivity toward children whose dinner consisted of high-fat fast foods. Focus on the "best," and why it's the best, rather than on meals that provide little in the way of nutrition.

Where did the different foods in these meals come from?

If your school is in a rural area, children may know quite a lot about the origins of food in agriculture and nature. On the other hand, some urban children may simply respond that food comes from the supermarket. If so, question them further about where food comes from.

Gifted Children

Ask gifted children to use the computer to research vegetarian diets. Ask them to find out how vegetarians can stay healthy without eating meat. Encourage children to present their findings to the class.

Preconceptions

Some children may assume that foods they like are good or nutritious. Explain that a food like cake may have ingredients from only two groups: grain products and milk products. It is all right to eat some cake, but other foods are needed too.

Have the children look at the food groups on page 24 of the Student Book. Ask:

What is the same about the food in each group?

What is different?

Once the children have been introduced to the four food groups, ask:

What other foods can you name?

Which group do these foods belong to?

Finally, encourage the children to think about the sources for the foods in each group. For instance, milk products come from mammals; vegetables and fruits and grain products come from plants; meat and alternatives come from animals and plants.

Exploration

Prepare a pizza.

1. Have all ingredients ready on a plate or in a bowl (in cubes, strips, or slices). Ask each child to assemble a pizza with a pita bread base. Encourage the children to use only ingredients they will eat. That way, the pizzas will vary and the food will not be wasted. Now have the children draw their pizza in their Science Journals.

2. Ask the children to consult the food guide in the Student Book. In their Science Journals, have the children classify each item in their pizza drawing according to food group. If any of the food groups are missing, have the children write the names.

3. Beside their drawing of the pizza, have the children list which ingredients come from plants and which come from animals.

Apply

What did we learn?

Exploration Results

Children should know that there are four food groups. All foods come from plants or animals. The foods in some groups come from either plants or animals, but the foods in other groups come from both.

Troubleshooting

Supervise children who are vegetarian or have dietary restrictions due to religion or food allergies when the pizzas are being assembled and eaten.

CURIOSITY PLACE

A milk-like beverage can be made from soybeans. This kind of milk does not come from mammals.

Have the children discuss the results of their pizza making. Ask them to suggest where the different foods on their pizza came from.

Explain that humans produce food by raising livestock, such as pigs, chickens, and cattle. Humans also plant crops, such as wheat and corn. However, humans do not always grow or raise food. They can also find food from wild plants and by fishing and hunting wild animals. Ask:

Where do we get the fruit we eat? the bread?

Where does the chicken in a chicken-salad sandwich come from?

Now ask the children to complete Reproducible 11A: *Where Does Food Come From?* (Answers: bread-wheat; peanut butter-peanuts; eggs-chickens; milk-cows; drumstick-chicken; corn on the cob-corn; cereal-wheat, corn or rice; cheese-cow; fish-fish; pickles-cucumber; grapes-grapevine)

Extending Learning

Encourage children to think about food production and the seasons. Ask them: When can we grow crops? Can we fish and hunt all year?

Ask the children if they know where pizza originated and then encourage discussion of other types of foods from other countries with which children might be familiar. It will be beneficial if you can spend some time discussing how various ethnic foods fall into the categories in Canada's Food Guide.

Apply

What did we learn?

Global Perspectives

Many people eat all the foods from the four food groups. They are omnivores. Other people are vegetarians. Most vegetarians eat everything but meat and fish, whereas a smaller group (vegans) do not eat any animal products (for example, eggs). People may choose a vegetarian diet for health reasons, out of concern for animal welfare, or for religious reasons (for example, Hindu teaching). Some choose a vegetarian or semi-vegetarian diet to preserve the Earth's resources. This is because raising animals for food uses more resources than does growing crops.

Integrating Science

More Science: Grow a Plant
Have the children grow an edible plant. Bean plants are good since they grow fast and vigorously. Encourage the children to document how long it takes from the planting of the seeds to the production of the food.

Performing Arts: Compose and Sing a Song
As a class, review the lyrics of "Old Macdonald Had a Farm." Then add new verses to the song, substituting other farm animals the class has learned about. Write the new lyrics on the board and have everyone sing.

Social Studies: Find Some Facts
Have children research the human life cycle in a very different place and culture. Ask the children to find out how tall people are, how old they live to be, and at what age they have babies. Discuss the findings in class.

THINK!

Ask the children to use the chart on Reproducible 11B: *What Do I Eat?* on page 76 to record what they eat in a day. Ask them to review what they ate and consider what they should eat. (Did they have foods from all food groups? Did they have too much meat and not enough milk?) Ask them to work in groups or with a family member to help them plan their meals for one day.

Where Does Food Come From?

Under each picture write animal or plant
to show where the food comes from.

Name _____ Date _____

What Do I Eat?

What do you eat in a day?
Put a check in the right box each time you
eat something from that food group.

Meals	Grains	Fruits and Vegetables	Milk	Meat and Alternatives	Other
breakfast					
lunch					
snack					
dinner					

How Do Humans Stay Healthy?

Student Book pages 26–27

In this lesson: Children learn what makes for a healthy lifestyle.

Outcomes

Children will have opportunities to:
- classify familiar animals according to similarities and differences in appearance, behaviour, and life cycles (T1)
- communicate observations, experiences, and thinking in a variety of ways (P3)
- classify objects, events, and organisms (P4)
- infer the probable outcome of an event or behaviour based on observations (P6)
- measure objects and events (P8)

Assessment

- Examine the children's Science Journals and review their notes and responses from the Exploration. (T1, P3, P4, P8)
- To assess their understanding of humans' needs, ask the children True or False questions such as the following (P6):

  All humans need to sleep at least eight hours a day. (false)

  To exercise, humans have to do sports. (false)

  Eating well is important to health. (true)

  Washing hands is a waste of time. (false)

  Sleeping well and eating a lot will make a human healthy, even with no exercise. (false)

Getting Organized

Materials: Reproducible 12: *What Is Missing?* on page 81; pictures of people exercising

Suggested Grouping: class, individual

Time Required: Activate 5–10 min; Explore 20–25 min; Apply 25–30 min

Advance Preparation: Collect pictures of people being active (for example, doing sports, housework, and gardening).

Safety: Warn children to tailor their health routines to their own physical needs. For instance, a child with asthma should not exercise very strenuously without first consulting a doctor.

Lesson Vocabulary

germ: a living thing that causes disease. Germs are too small for the eye to see.

Activate

What do we know? What do we want to know?

Content Background

Exercise is very important to health. It strengthens the muscles as well as the circulatory and respiratory systems. Exercise also helps to offset the physical effects of stress, which can cause illness. Another role of exercise is to reduce or maintain weight. Excess weight is linked to heart disease, diabetes, high blood pressure, and other illnesses.

Personal hygiene, or keeping clean, is also essential to good health. Regular washing controls bacteria and germs and stops skin infections. Frequently washing your hands and keeping them away from your eyes, nose, and mouth help to avert viruses, such as the common cold. Good dental hygiene slows or prevents tooth decay and gum disease.

Sleep is marked by loss of consciousness and a decreased response to outside stimulation. For the average adult, six to nine hours of sleep is considered normal; a child of seven or eight often needs about 10 hours of sleep. When people are deprived of sleep, they may experience fatigue, poor memory, and irritability. Interestingly, though, lack of sleep does not seem to create long-term psychological or physical damage.

Of course, as stressed in the previous lesson, eating a balanced diet from the four food groups is also an important part of maintaining good health.

Explain to the children that being healthy means feeling good and functioning well in every aspect of life (i.e., having plenty of energy for school and play, and being helpful to the family at home). Ask:

What can we do to keep ourselves feeling healthy?

Write the answers on the board. Pass around pictures that show exercising (not only of sports but also less obvious exercise like gardening and housework). Ask:

Are sports the only kind of exercise we can do?

Children With Special Needs

What are the health needs of people with physical disabilities? If you have children with physical disabilities in your class and you feel it is appropriate, ask them to comment. Children can, but need not, describe their own health regime (it will not always differ from other children's). Have children find out about the needs of people with limited mobility. How do they exercise? Do they need the same diet as other people? If children feel comfortable, they can present their results to the class.

CURIOSITY PLACE

Our ideas and feelings can affect our health. Feeling cheerful and thinking happy thoughts helps us stay healthy.

Explore

Encourage the children to think about people or animals they have seen sleeping. Ask:

Did the people or animals tremble?

Did their eyelids flicker?

Explain that these people or animals were in REM (rapid eye movement) sleep. The most physical activity during sleep happens during REM sleep.

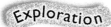

Create a class graph.

1. Have the children study the graph on page 27 of the Student Book. Point out the two axes. Ask for volunteers to make an identical graph on the board.

2. In their Science Journals, have the children record the time they go to bed at night and the time they wake up. Have them count the number of hours in between and record the number in their journals.

3. Now read out each number of hours slept listed along the bottom of the graph. As you read out each number, have the children who sleep that number of hours raise their hands. You can ask the class to help you count how many children respond each time. Mark the numbers on the graph.

4. Ask the class which is the most common number of hours slept. Which is the least common? Point out that the children can sleep different hours and still be healthy. Ask:

What is the right amount of sleep for you?

How can you tell?

Children can reply in their Science Journals.

Troubleshooting

Some children may not sleep the same number of hours every night, or not always at the same time. For step 2, ask these children to work with the numbers that are most common for them.

Exploration Results

Children should discover how many hours they sleep a night. Everyone needs sleep, but sleep patterns vary. Children can remain healthy in spite of different sleep patterns.

Preconceptions

Children may assume that looking after their health in just a few ways is enough. This lesson should convey that keeping healthy involves a whole range of behaviours.

Apply

What did we learn?

Remind the children that sleep alone does not make for good health. All aspects of a human's lifestyle affect health: sleep, diet, cleanliness, grooming, and exercise. Ask:

> **Do you think a human who sleeps well but barely eats is likely to be healthy?**
>
> **What about a human who sleeps enough but does not keep clean?**

Pass out Reproducible 12: *What Is Missing?* and have the children work on it. Ask the children if they can think of any other factors that contribute to good health. Encourage them to mention dressing appropriately. For instance, going outside in shorts on a cold winter day could affect a person's health.

Extending Learning

Have children research how the health needs of humans compare with those of other animals. Do all animals need to sleep, eat, exercise, and clean themselves? Ask the children to recall hibernation and migration. Ask:

> **Does a hibernating animal need exercise? a migrating animal?**
>
> **How do animals stay healthy without wearing clothing?**
>
> **Is the way animals keep warm less wasteful than the way humans do?**

Global Perspectives

Staying healthy involves adapting to one's environment. In Mediterranean countries, such as Greece and Italy, many people sleep during the hottest part of the day, the afternoon. They then stay up late to enjoy the cooler night air. As a result, people in hot climates often sleep fewer hours at night than do most people in cold climates.

Integrating Science

Language Arts: Keep a Journal
Have children keep a dream journal for a week. They should record their dreams in the journal every morning, right after waking up. At the end of the week, the children can divide up into small groups to share and compare their dreams. Note: Children should share their dreams only if they wish to do so.

Physical Education: Get Some Exercise
Lead the class in an exercise routine that includes aerobic and muscle-building exercises. Explain the function of each exercise (for example, strengthens lungs and heart, improves muscle tone in thighs).

THINK!
You need to get enough sleep so that you will have enough energy to work, play, and help others.

What Is Missing?

To stay healthy, humans need to eat, sleep, exercise, and keep clean. What has each person forgotten to do? Write the answers in the blanks.

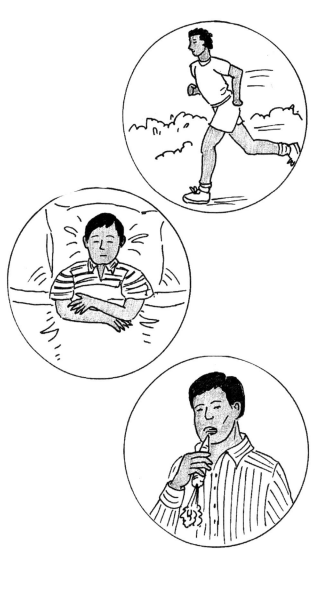

_____   _____

Have you had a healthy day today?

How Do Humans Affect Other Animals?

Student Book pages 28–29

In this lesson: Children investigate how humans affect other animals.

Outcomes

Children will have opportunities to:
- classify familiar animals according to similarities and differences in appearance, behaviour, and life cycles (T1)
- describe how animals are important in the lives of Aboriginal peoples in BC (T3)
- describe ways in which animals are important to other living things and the environment (T4)
- communicate observations, experiences, and thinking in a variety of ways (P3)
- classify objects, events, and organisms (P4)
- use their senses to interpret observations (P5)
- show respect for Aboriginal peoples and other cultures (A4)

Assessment

- Assess students' scripts. (T1, P3, P4, P6)
- Observe children as they listen to your Aboriginal visitor. Check the questions they prepare ahead of time and the notes and booklets they prepare later. (T3, T4, A4)
- Check students' work on Reproducible 13A: *A Special Time* on page 88 to assess whether they understand the importance of animals to BC Aboriginal Peoples. (T3, T4, A4)
- Check students' work on Reproducible 13C: *Can We Live Here?* on page 90 to assess whether they understand the importance of animals to other living things. (T4, P5)

Getting Organized

Materials: Reproducibles 13A: *A Special Time* on page 88, 13B: *Animals Help Us* on page 89, 13C: *Can We Live Here?* on page 89, and 13D: *How Do We Survive?* on page 91

Suggested Grouping: class, individual

Time Required: Activate 10–15 min; Explore 30–35 min; Apply 25–30 min

Advance Preparation: none

Lesson Vocabulary

endangered animal: An endangered animal is one that may disappear from the Earth.

extinct: An animal is extinct if it no longer exists on the Earth.

CURIOSITY PLACE

In the 1950s, polar bears were becoming endangered because of hunting. A group of people worldwide helped to limit the hunting of polar bears, and as a result, polar bears are no longer endangered, but they are still vulnerable. Climate change is causing the ice floes to melt earlier. Polar bears depend on ice floes for access to their prey and therefore they are not getting enough food.

Activate

What do we know? What do we want to know? What do we know?

Content Background

Humans have affected the natural world more than any other animal. As a species, humans are clever and adaptable. These advantages have enabled us to alter the environment of other animals, sometimes drastically.

Humans are multiplying very rapidly. As the human population grows, undeveloped land is claimed and built on or farmed. Animal habitats are thereby reduced or altered. As animals at the top of the food chain, humans also consume other animals for food and use their body parts for clothing, decorations, and trophies.

Some ways that humans affect animals are more subtle. Farming and industry provide food and jobs for humans, yet both also create pollution that harms other animals (and sometimes humans, too). For instance, farm pesticides and industrial byproducts can pollute water that animals drink or inhabit. Humans also introduce alien species into natural environments either deliberately or accidentally. For example, the zebra mussels that humans brought on boats by chance into Lake Ontario changed the ecology of the lake. Even small changes to an animal's environment can threaten the health and well-being of a species.

In Canada, many species are in danger of becoming extinct. Of the 600 species of birds, 49 are at risk; 53 of the 194 mammals; 64 of the 3269 plants; and 53 of the 1000 fish are endangered. There may be many more species at risk but the official committee can go through only so many a year.

Have the children visualize their homes and the immediate surroundings. Suggest that many living things are there, even though the children may not be aware of all of them. Ask:

What kinds of living things are outside your home?

Are there also living things besides people inside your home?

Record the answers on the board. Then ask:

Do you affect these living things? How?

Introduce the idea that we are not always aware of how we affect other living things. For instance, we deliberately provide food and shelter for a pet dog. However, if we pave over the garden to make a patio, we may inadvertently be killing plants that birds or rabbits use as food.

Now ask the children if they can think of items that living things provide for us. Children may think of food, which has already been discussed in Lesson 11. Encourage them to think of clothing and furnishings made from things like leather, wool, feathers. Have them provide an example of each. (Be prepared for some children to be aware of objections to the use of leather in clothing and furniture.)

Preconceptions

Children may recognize that we affect other living things but not realize that other living things affect us too. Stress the idea of interdependence. For instance, humans need fish as a source of food and worms to aerate the soil so that crops can grow.

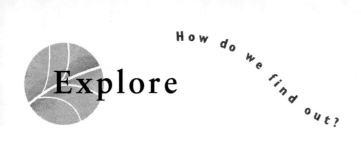

Ask the class:

Do you think more animals live in the city or in the country? Why?

Are there any animals that like to live near humans?
(Some scavengers, like raccoons and gulls, like to live near humans.)

Have you ever helped an animal? How have animals helped you?

Encourage the children to discover the link between human populations and activity and the presence of other life forms. Understanding this link will help them to interpret the frames in the movie reel.

It is important, too, to help children to understand that, unlike humans, animals do not and cannot choose to help or harm others. They operate on the basis of instinct. Children should understand that all animals should be approached with respect and caution. Even pets still retain some instincts from the wild and can strike out at people if provoked or frightened.

Write a movie script.

1. Have the children open their Student Book to pages 28–29. Ask them to examine each picture carefully. Encourage them to notice how many plants and animals are in each frame and what signs of human activity are visible. Now have them write a script in their Science Journals. An older student or parent volunteer could help transcribe the script for students. The script should state whether what is happening in each frame is good or bad for other living things.

   Alternatively, you may wish to suggest that the children choose an animal and

write the script from the point of view of that animal. They could, as well, go through the pictures in reverse order, telling how their lush paradise became a barren, unlivable area. (In the second scene, the children could be digging up and removing the plants, rather than planting them.) Having the children use their imaginations in this way may help them get beyond the anthropocentric point of view that tends to be prevalent, particularly at younger ages. Their understanding should be deepened if you help them to feel that they are a part of the natural world rather than its "master." It will also be a start toward understanding the point of view of Aboriginal cultures in which humans are seen as part of a whole, affecting and being affected by other animals in a cycle.

2. Give the children a few minutes to practise reading their scripts. Then ask each child to read his or her script aloud to the class. Invite the class to comment on each script. Make sure to correct any misconceptions.

Troubleshooting

Ensure the children treat the frames of the reel as a continuum and not as unrelated images.

Exploration Results

Children should discover that the more space humans take up, the less space there is for other living things. Some human inventions damage or destroy other life forms. Humans can also create positive surroundings for animals. They can plant trees and shrubs for food and provide water for drinking and bathing.

While children are considering their relationship to other animals, this would be a good time to focus on the curriculum outcome that asks children to describe the special relationship that Aboriginal peoples in BC have with animals.

You will find a treasury of information on the Fort Nelson Aboriginal Project website (see page 11). To fill out the children's experience, read *Little Water and the Gift of the Animals* and have them complete Reproducible 13B: *Animals Help Us* on page 89.

Distribute Reproducible 13A: *A Special Time* on page 88. You may wish to spend some class time reading the Reproducible with the children and discussing ceremonies. Point out that some are used for happy times (birthdays, weddings), while others are used at very sad times (funerals). Lead the children to understand that they are often occasions for expressing deeply held feelings.

This will be an excellent opportunity for children from other cultures to share information about ceremonies that are important to them. It should be a time of respectful sharing, of appreciation for the traditions of other cultures.

Follow your School Board's established protocol for inviting a member of the local Aboriginal community into your classroom. Suggest that the individual might speak with the children about his or her community's relationship with animals and related traditions and ceremonies. Give your visitor plenty of warning and offer as broad a time frame as you can within which he or she can choose to visit. Ask how much class time he or she is able to give you. (You may need to devote more than one lesson to these ideas. You may also find that you will cover the concept of sustainability that is currently brought out on page 94.) Your visitor would probably also find a checklist of this unit's learning outcomes useful for perusal before the visit.

Discuss the visit with the children ahead of time and as a class, develop some questions you might ask. Discuss with the class how they would like to be treated if they were a visitor and what they might do to make their visitor feel welcomed and respected.

Following the visit, you might compose a class letter to be sent as a thank-you. You may also wish to provide library and computer time so that the children can do further research on the roles animals have played in the lives of Aboriginal peoples in BC. They might use their findings and the notes they made during the speaker's visit to make descriptive booklets, if your visitor considers this appropriate. Otherwise, they might simply use their own findings. The following website is helpful:
http://142.27.32.42/~fnap/fnaphome.html

Global Perspectives

Canadians consume more than people in most other parts of the world. As a rule, we live in houses that are bigger than we need, depend too much on cars, and are generally more wasteful than people in many other countries. In India, for example, many generations of a family often live together in one house. In China, many people ride bicycles to work. Using fewer resources would lessen our negative impact on other animals.

Apply

What did we learn?

Encourage the children to describe the features in the Student Book illustrations that support the health and growth of animals. Ask:

> **Are animals living here now? Why?**
>
> **What other places do you know where animals live? What makes these places suitable?**
>
> **How would you plan a zoo that would be a healthy place for animals to live?**

Then explain that changing an animal's habitat can harm or help it. Give these examples:

> **Bears and moose need to live in the woods. What would happen if we cut down the trees?**
>
> **How would fish be affected if we cleaned up dirty lakes?**
>
> **What might happen to squirrels and birds if we cut down the trees in which they build their nests?**

To avoid oversimplifying this issue, you might want to point out to the children that we cut trees to build houses and furniture that we need. Lakes become dirty as a result of processes used to manufacture cars and other products we either need or want. Children can be encouraged to understand the effects of our actions and to become part of a solution to the problem by being aware and by using strategies of conservation as they grow older.

Have the children complete Reproducible 13C: *Can We Live Here?*

Extending Learning

Ask children what happens if an animal's habitat is badly damaged. Introduce the idea of extinction. Remind the children of how animals develop from an egg, and explain that an egg may not be able to develop in poor conditions. Show the children pictures of some animals that have recently become extinct.

Tell the children that we can sometimes save animals that are in danger of becoming extinct, if we act swiftly. A species of animal that is close to extinction is called an endangered species. Environmental groups around the world keep track of animal populations and try to alert human beings to the fact that certain animals are endangered in the hope that steps can be taken to reverse the trend.

Plan to have materials available in your school library so that children can choose an endangered animal and find information about it. Have them work in pairs and compare an endangered species with one whose population seems to be growing. You may wish to distribute Reproducible 13D: *How Do We Survive?* on page 91, which you can discuss as a class on completion. If you wish to print materials ahead of time for the children to use, there are many websites devoted to this subject area. The resource section provides websites specifically related to endangered animals in British Columbia. You might have the children choose different endangered animals, including some from other parts of the world. If there is an organization or government body to which children could address their concerns, help them to compose a class letter to send out.

Integrating Science

Art: Model Animals
Ask children to rcmember a good relationship they have had with an animal (for example, a pet, a wild animal near their home). Have children model themselves interacting with the animal. They can use clay, recycled or found materials to make their models.

More Science: Talk to an Expert
Invite an environmentalist to visit the class to discuss local habitat damage (for example, from construction) and its effect on animals. Discuss ways to improve a local animal habitat.

THINK!
To care for a pet, you must provide or re-create many of the things the animal would find in its natural habitat.

Name _____ Date _____

A Special Time

We all have special times that are important to us. We show that they are important by having a ceremony each time they occur. For example, at birthdays, we often have a birthday cake and sing happy birthday. Tell about a ceremony that is important to you, your family, or your community. In my family we have a special ceremony when we celebrate

_____ .

This is what we do:

_____

_____

Aboriginal communities have ceremonies that show how important animals are to them. For example, many communities have a First Salmon Ceremony. This celebrates the yearly return of the salmon and the People's relationship with them as part of the circle of life. Aboriginal people have a special ceremony to honour these animals:

_____ This is what they do: _____

_____

_____

_____ This is what they do: _____

_____

Name ____________________ Date ____________________

Reproducible 13B

Animals Help Us

List the animals in the story as your teacher reads it to you. Would they have been hunted by Aboriginal people to help them survive?
Use the chart below to decide how the Aboriginal people used certain animals.

Add any other animals to your chart that you learn about from your teacher.

Animal	Clothing	Food	Tools
wolf			
deer			
bear			
hawk			
turtle			
otter			

Can We Live Here?

Circle any animals that have what they need to survive.
Draw in what the other animals are missing.
Cross out anything that may be harming the animals.

How Do We Survive?

With your partner, find information that will help you make notes beside the headings below. Try to figure out why one species is endangered while the other one isn't.

	Endangered Species	Species that Is Doing Well
Where it lives	_____	_____
	_____	_____
	_____	_____
What it eats	_____	_____
	_____	_____
	_____	_____
Why it is endangered	_____	_____
	_____	_____
	_____	_____
	_____	_____
	_____	_____
or		
Why its population is growing	_____	_____
	_____	_____
	_____	_____
How we can we help	_____	_____
	_____	_____
	_____	_____

How Do Life Cycles Compare?

Student Book pages 30–31

In this lesson: Children compare the life cycles of different animals.

Outcomes

Children will have opportunities to:
- classify familiar animals according to similarities and differences in appearance, behaviour, and life cycles (T1)
- describe some changes that affect animals (T2)
- describe ways in which animals are important to other living things and the environment (T4)
- communicate observations, experiences, and thinking in a variety of ways (P3)
- classify objects, events, and organisms (P4)
- infer the probable outcome of an event or behaviour based on observations (P6)
- show respect for Aboriginal peoples and other cultures (A4)

Assessment

- The Extending Learning will help you assess children's ability to describe changes that affect animals. (T2)
- Reproducible 14C: *Animals Grow* is a test that you can use to help assess how well students understand the basic concepts in *Animals Grow*. (T1, T4, P4)
- Have the children submit their Science Journals. You can use each child's six drawings of the life cycle to assess understanding of the classes of mammal, reptile, and fish, and the different phases in their life cycles. (T1, T4, P3, P4, P6, A4)

Getting Organized

Materials: Reproducible 14A: *What Kind of Animal?* on page 97 and Reproducible 14B: *How Do We Help One Another?* on page 98

Suggested Grouping: class, small groups, individual

Time Required: Activate 10–15 min; Explore 35–40 min; Apply 35–40 min

Advance Preparation: none

Safety: Have children pair off for the walk outside the school.

Lesson Vocabulary

reptile: a cold-blooded animal that has dry, thick skin and breathes with lungs. The female usually expels eggs that hatch outside her body. Snakes, turtles, and crocodiles are examples of reptiles.

Content Background

Fish were the first vertebrates, or animals with backbones. Female fish usually release their eggs into the water. The eggs are then fertilized by milt, or sperm, cast out by the males. In some species, the male or female then picks up the eggs and carries them until they hatch (for example, cichlids). Some fish, such as eel and salmon, travel long distances to lay their eggs.

Reptiles are also vertebrates. They evolved from amphibians and lived in water at first. Now reptiles no longer lay their eggs in water, and their embryos do not develop there. Eggs are fertilized inside the female's body. Most female reptiles then lay the eggs in a safe place and leave them to develop. All reptiles have dry, thick skin without glands, but reptiles come in many forms. Snakes, turtles, iguanas, and crocodiles are all reptiles.

Birds and mammals evolved from ancient reptiles. Unlike reptiles, though, mammals and birds are warm-blooded. Being able to regulate their body temperatures has made mammals and birds more adaptable than reptiles.

Activate

What do we know? What do we want to know?

Have the children recall the different classes of animals they have studied in *Animals Grow* (mammal, bird, amphibian, and so on). Ask:

Which types of animals begin life as an egg?
(all)

Does the egg develop inside or outside the mother?
(the eggs of all but mammals develop outside the body)

Record the correct replies on the board. Now prompt the children to remember how animals grow and change throughout the life cycle. Ask:

How does a butterfly change and grow? a robin? a frog? a human?

CURIOSITY PLACE

Long ago, reptiles lived on the Earth before birds or mammals. Birds and mammals developed from reptiles.

Explore

How do we find out?

Read the text of the Student Book on page 30. Children may already have begun to describe mammals, reptiles, or fish in the Activate phase. Use whatever details you recorded on the board to enlarge the description of each animal class. Ask:

How is a mammal different from any other animal?
(It nurses its young from mammary glands; it has hair; the eggs usually develop inside the mother.)

Explain what a reptile is and give examples (turtles, snakes, crocodiles, and so on). Then ask:

How is a reptile different from a mammal?
(It has dry skin; it is cold-blooded; the female usually expels eggs that hatch outside her body.)

What way do fish differ from mammals and reptiles?
(They live and breathe underwater.)

Write the answers on the board.

Exploration

Find similar life stages.

1. Have children choose a mammal at one stage of the life cycle (not the egg stage) and draw it in their Science Journals. The mammal must not be the mouse illustrated in the Student Book. Remind children to depict the mammal as accurately as possible, showing those features that change and those that stay the same during the mammal's life cycle. As the children are drawing, walk around the class to ensure that the animals chosen are all mammals. Now ask the children to draw the phase in the life cycle that came before the one they have chosen.
2. Now invite the children to choose and draw a reptile at a stage in its life cycle (not the egg stage). The reptile must not be a snake,

which is illustrated in the Student Book. Again, stress accuracy. Check that all chosen animals are reptiles before children draw an earlier phase in the animal's life cycle. Watch out for children's confusion between reptiles and amphibians.

3. Finally, have the children select and draw a fish at a stage in its life cycle (not the egg stage). Do not allow the children to simply copy the illustration from the Student Book. Now have the children draw an earlier phase in the fish life cycle.

4. Select several children to show their drawings of a mammal to the class, others a reptile, and others a fish. Using the sample drawings, the class should describe the life cycle of each class of animal. Make sure children point out basic similarities and differences in the development of each class of animal.

Troubleshooting

Consider having the children depict the same phases of the life cycle for each of the animals they are drawing. For instance, one child could show fully grown adult animals and another child could show baby animals. This may be less confusing for children than representing different phases of the life cycle for the animals. It should also ensure that all phases of the life cycle are drawn and can be used for class discussion.

Exploration Results

Through their drawings in their Science Journals, children should demonstrate an understanding of the basic features of mammals, reptiles, and fish. They should appreciate that animals grow and change throughout the life cycle and that some features of an animal remain constant while others change. Children should now be able to identify the most significant differences in the life cycles of the three classes of animals.

Discuss with the children why it is useful to sort animals into groups such as mammals, reptiles, and fish. Have them consider the task of putting away their own laundry. They might have one place for socks, one place for underwear, another place for T-shirts. They know immediately where each item goes, and when they look in that particular place, they can predict exactly what they will find there. Similarly, if scientists find an animal that hasn't been seen before, they can observe it to decide which category it fits into. Others will then be able to predict certain things about that animal. Similarly, if you know which class an animal belongs to, you can predict certain things about its life cycle.

Apply

What did we learn?

Have children look at the illustrations on pages 30–31 of the Student Book. Encourage them to compare the life cycles in the book with those in their Science Journals. Now ask the children to match the life cycles of the same classes of animal. Have them record the results in their Science Journals.

Have the children complete Reproducible 14A: *What Kind of Animal?* Ask:

How are the life cycles shown similar?

How are they different?

What other kinds of animals have similar life cycles?

Have the children look back through the unit and either select another animal or an animal of their choice. (You might encourage struggling learners to select from the unit, as the information and visuals will give them a headstart.) Encourage others to consider an unusual animal from elsewhere in the world, e.g., pandas, whales, parrots, and so on. Provide library time for the children to find information about the animal and draw its life cycle on art or poster paper. They should reserve a section of the paper on which to write any notes they'd like to include about the animal: interesting features, foods, habitat, and so on.

Check their work for scientific accuracy and then bind all of the pages into a portfolio of animal life cycles for display in the classroom.

Extending Learning

Explain to children that animals of different types may affect one another's survival. For instance, a bear in British Columbia may eat salmon to survive. If humans eat too much salmon, the bear may not be able to find any. If a beaver cuts down a tree for its dam, the dead log will create a place for insects to live.

Now have children do Reproducible 14B: *How Do We Help One Another?* Talk about the results.

This would be another good point at which to invite a representative from an Aboriginal community to visit the class, this time to focus more on the concept of sustainability. You might also use the resources listed on page 11. Your visitor may be able to help the children to appreciate their own place in the cycle of life, i.e., we help other animals, not simply because it makes us feel good or because we feel it's the right thing to do, but because the loss of that animal will have repercussions throughout the food chain and will eventually affect us.

Apply

What did we learn?

Global Perspectives

Humans are not the only social animals. Whales and dolphins live in pods, elephants in herds, and lions in prides. Less known are the colonies formed by farm and alley cats. Females nurse and tend one another's kittens. Generations of the same family often share a territory.

THINK!
Like a cat, a human is born live from an egg that develops inside the mother. A human mother cares for and nurses her baby. A human grows, becomes able to reproduce, and later ages and dies.

Integrating Science

Language Arts: Write a Riddle
Divide the children into groups of three or four. Ask each group to choose an animal and write a riddle about it. The riddle should have important clues about the specific animal and also the class to which it belongs. Try to answer the riddles as a class.

More Science: Research and Share
Ask each child to pick an animal and find out how long that animal has existed. Has it changed over time? How? Each child should then write a paragraph about the animal researched. Paragraphs can be read aloud to the class.

Art: Animals in Art
Read *Haida Art,* George F. MacDonald. (Douglas & McIntyre, 1999). You might want to borrow the book from a local library and keep it available in the classroom for the children to enjoy. The book illustrates how Northwest Coast First Nations people depict animals in art.

Reproducible

14A

What Kind of Animal?

Amphibians, insects, and birds are three
kinds of animals. Draw lines between the
animals that belong to the same group.
Under each animal, write the correct label.

Amphibian   Bird   Insect

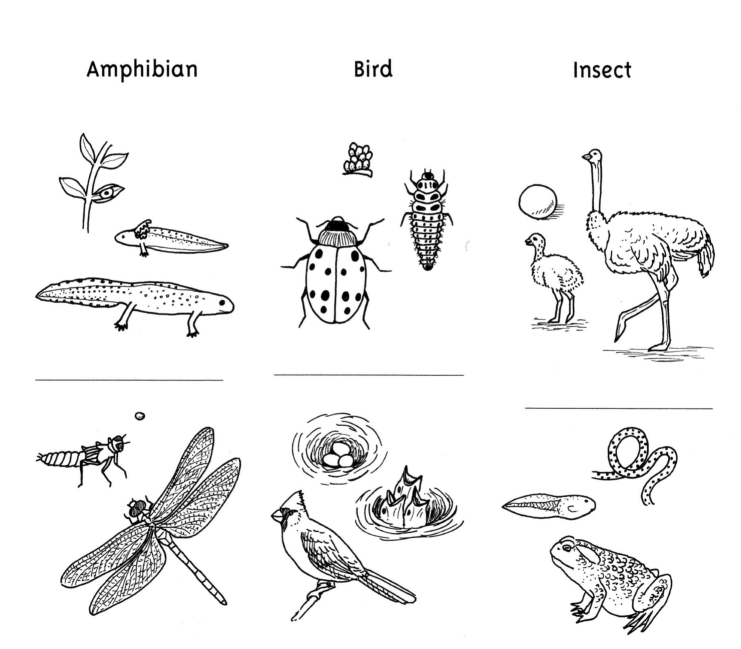

_____   _____

                                            _____

Name _____   Date _____

How Do We Help One Another?

Animals depend on one another. How are the
animals in the picture helping one another?
List the ways at the bottom of the page.

_____

_____

_____

Animals Grow

1. Choose an animal and draw it in different stages of its life.

_____

_____

_____

_____

2. Where does your animal live?
   What characteristics does the animal have
   to help it live there?

_____

_____

_____

_____

3. Write or draw three ways humans can
   help animals.

_____

_____

_____

_____

Prescribed Learning Outcomes

Animals Grow (Animal Growth and Changes)

You can use this rubric to generally assess Prescribed Learning Outcomes

T1   classify familiar animals according to similarities and differences in appearance, behaviour, and life cycles

T2   describe some changes that affect animals

T3   describe how animals are important in the lives of Aboriginal peoples in BC

T4   describe ways in which animals are important to other living things and the environment

The student:

Level 1	Level 2	Level 3	Level 4
classifies familiar animals according to similarities and differences in appearance, behaviour, and life cycles **with major misconceptions and little detail** (*identifies different types of animals, how they care for young*)	classifies familiar animals according to similarities and differences in appearance, behaviour, and life cycles **with minor misconceptions and some detail** (*identifies different types of animals, how they care for young*)	classifies familiar animals according to similarities and differences in appearance, behaviour, and life cycles **accurately with details** (*identifies different types of animals, how they care for young*)	classifies familiar animals according to similarities and differences in appearance, behaviour, and life cycles accurately **with precision and details** (*identifies different types of animals, how they care for young*)
describes some changes that affect animals **with major misconceptions and little detail** (*meaning of hibernation, migration, endangered species*)	describes some changes that affect animals **with minor misconceptions and some detail** (*meaning of hibernation, migration, endangered species*)	describes some changes that affect animals **accurately with details** (*meaning of hibernation, migration, endangered species*)	describes some changes that affect animals accurately **with precision and details** (*meaning of hibernation, migration, endangered species*)
describes how animals are important in the lives of Aboriginal peoples in BC **with major misconceptions and little detail** (*used for clothing, cooking, and to make weapons*)	describes how animals are important in the lives of Aboriginal peoples in BC **with minor misconceptions and some detail** (*used for clothing, cooking, and to make weapons*)	describes how animals are important in the lives of Aboriginal peoples in BC **accurately with details** (*used for clothing, cooking, and to make weapons*)	describes how animals are important in the lives of Aboriginal peoples in BC accurately **with precision and details** (*used for clothing, cooking, and to make weapons*)
describes ways in which animals are important to other living things and the environment **with major misconceptions and little detail** (*feeding wild birds, animals feeding on those lower down the food chain*)	describes ways in which animals are important to other living things and the environment **with minor misconceptions and some detail** (*feeding wild birds, animals feeding on those lower down the food chain*)	describes ways in which animals are important to other living things and the environment **accurately with details** (*feeding wild birds, animals feeding on those lower down the food chain*)	describes ways in which animals are important to other living things and the environment accurately **with precision and details** (*feeding wild birds, animals feeding on those lower down the food chain*)
explains concepts **with major misconceptions and little detail** (*Science Journal, classification system, Think! answers, discussions, reproducible pages, charts, etc.*)	explains concepts **with minor misconceptions and some details** (*Science Journal, classification system, Think! answers, reproducible pages, discussions, charts, etc.*)	explains concepts **accurately with details** (*Science Journal, classification system, Think! answers, reproducible pages, charts, discussions, etc.*)	explains concepts **accurately with precision and details,** (*Science Journal, classification system, Think! answers, reproducible pages, charts, discussions, etc.*)
rarely uses Science Inquiry skills; requires **teacher assistance** (*to compare and classify characteristics of different animals and how they grow, etc.*)	**sometimes** uses Science Inquiry skills; requires **some teacher assistance** (*to compare and classify characteristics of different animals and how they grow, etc.*)	**usually** uses Science Inquiry skills **independently** (*to compare and classify characteristics of different animal and how they grow,, etc.*)	**consistently** uses Science Inquiry skills **independently** (*to compare and classify characteristics of different animals and how they grow, etc.*)
rarely communicates learning about animals and their characteristics **accurately**	**sometimes** communicates learning about animals and their characteristics **accurately with some details**	**usually** communicates learning about animals and their characteristics **accurately** and **with details**	**consistently** communicates learning about animals and their characteristics **accurately with precision and clarity**
uses **a few** science and technology terms (*egg, pupa, larva, adult, life cycle, etc.*) and units of measurement **appropriately**	uses **some** science and technology terms (*egg, pupa, larva, adult, life cycle, etc.*) and units of measurement **appropriately**	uses **many** science and technology terms (*egg, pupa, larva, adult, life cycle, etc.*) and units of measurement **appropriately**	uses **most or all** science and technology terms (*egg, pupa, larva, adult, life cycle, etc.*) and units of measurement **appropriately**
rarely makes connections to the real world; requires **teacher assistance** (*identifies the needs of an animal, the effects of humans on animals, etc.*)	**sometimes** makes connections to the real world; requires **some teacher assistance** (*identifies the needs of an animal, the effects of humans on animals, etc.*)	**usually** makes connections to the real world that are **accurate, detailed, and include examples** (*identifies the needs of an animal, the effects of humans on animals, etc.*)	**consistently** makes connections to the real world that are **accurate, detailed, and include illustrative examples** (*identifies the needs of an animal, the effects of humans on animals, etc.*)

Process/Attitude Outcomes

Animals Grow (Animal Growth and Change)

You can use this Rubric to generally assess the following outcomes.
P5   use their senses to interpret observations
P6   infer the probable outcome of an event or behaviour based on observations
A4   show respect for Aboriginal peoples and other cultures

The student:

Level 1	Level 2	Level 3	Level 4
uses their senses to interpret observations **with teacher prompting** (*makes practical use of observations*)	uses their senses to interpret observations **with some teacher prompting** (*makes practical use of observations*)	uses their senses to interpret observations **with little teacher prompting** (*makes practical use of observations*)	uses their senses to interpret observations **independently** (*makes practical use of observations*)
rarely infers the probable outcome of an event or behaviour based on observations (*moves from observed sequences of events to unseen sequences of events*)	**sometimes** infers the probable outcome of an event or behaviour based on observations (*moves from observed sequences of events to unseen sequences of events*)	**usually** infers the probable outcome of an event or behaviour based on observations (*moves from observed sequences of events to unseen sequences of events*) shows **some** respect for all cultures (*awareness of other cultures, appreciation of the contributions of other cultures*)	**consistently** infers the probable outcome of an event or behaviour based on observations (*moves from observed sequences of events to unseen sequences of events*)
requires prompting to show respect for all cultures (*awareness of other cultures, appreciation of the contributions of other cultures*)	shows **some** respect for all cultures (*awareness of other cultures, appreciation of the contributions of other cultures*)	**usually** shows respect for all cultures (*awareness of other cultures, appreciation of the contributions of other cultures*)	**consistently** shows respect for all cultures (*awareness of other cultures, appreciation of the contributions of other cultures*)

Culminating Activity

To assess the skills students used during the culminating activity, use the Design Process Rubric, the Communicating Rubric, and Presentation Rubric in the *Program and Assessment Guide.*

The student:

Level 1	Level 2	Level 3	Level 4
draws a stage of an animal's life and then the rest of the life cycle **with teacher assistance**	draws a stage of an animal's life and then the rest of the life cycle **with some assistance from teacher or classmate**	draws a stage of an animal's life and then the rest of the life cycle **with little or no assistance**	draws a stage of an animal's life and then the rest of the life cycle **independently**
compares life cycles of different animals **with teacher assistance**	compares life cycles of different animals **with some assistance from teacher or classmate**	compares life cycles of different animals **with little or no assistance**	compares life cycles of different animals **independently**
follows instructions **with teacher assistance**	follows the steps of their plan **with some assistance from teacher or classmate**; selects **mostly appropriate** materials	follows the steps of their plan **with little or no assistance**; selects **appropriate** materials	follows the steps of their plan **independently**; selects **the most appropriate** materials
applies **a few** of the following concepts when comparing and drawing life cycle:	applies **some** of the following concepts when comparing and drawing life cycle:	applies **most** of the following concepts when comparing and drawing life cycle:	applies **all** or **almost all** of the following concepts when comparing and drawing life cycle:
the stages of the life cycle of a variety of animals	the stages of the life cycle of a variety of animals	the stages of the life cycle of a variety of animals	the stages of the life cycle of a variety of animals
animals' appearance and activities change through their life cycle	animals' appearance and activities change through their life cycle	animals' appearance and activities change through their life cycle	animals' appearance and activities change through their life cycle
the characteristics of a variety of mammals, reptiles, insects, etc.	the characteristics of a variety of mammals, reptiles, insects, etc.	the characteristics of a variety of mammals, reptiles, insects, etc.	the characteristics of a variety of mammals, reptiles, insects, etc.
some characteristics of animals are constant	some characteristics of animals are constant	some characteristics of animals are constant	some characteristics of animals are constant
compares life cycle drawings with those of other students, noting **a few** of the similarities and differences of the life cycles	compares life cycle drawings with those of other students, noting **some** of the similarities and differences of the life cycles	compares life cycle drawings with those of other students, noting **many** of the similarities and differences of the life cycles	compares life cycle drawings with those of other students, noting **most** of the similarities and differences of the life cycles
explains the different stages of life cycles **with little detail**; requires **prompting**	explains the different stages of life cycles **with some detail**; requires **some prompting**	explains the different stages of life cycles **clearly with most details**; requires **little prompting**	explains the different stages of life cycles **clearly, precisely, and with complete details**
rarely uses science and technology terms *(egg, larva, pupa, adult, etc.)* **accurately**	**sometimes** uses science and technology terms *(egg, larva, pupa, adult, etc.)* **accurately**	**usually** uses science and technology terms *(egg, larva, pupa, adult, etc.)* **accurately**	**consistently** uses science and technology terms *(egg, larva, pupa, adult, etc.)* **accurately**
explains how animals interact with each other and with the environment **with teacher assistance**	explains how animals interact with each other and with the environment **with some assistance from teacher or classmate**	explains how animals interact with each other and with the environment **with little or no assistance**	explains how animals interact with each other and with the environment **independently**
describes **with teacher assistance** how society in general uses animals and how Aboriginal peoples in BC use them	describes, **with some assistance from teacher or classmate,** how society in general uses animals and how Aboriginal peoples in BC use them	describes, **with little or no assistance,** how society in general uses animals and how Aboriginal peoples in BC use them	describes **independently** how society in general uses animals and how Aboriginal peoples in BC use them